Cardinal's
Handbook
Of
Recipe
Development

Evelyn Hullah, B.H. Sc.

Senior Home Economist
of Cardinal Kitchens and
Vice-President of Cardinal
Biologicals Ltd., Evelyn
Hullah has conducted extensive recipe development
projects as a consultant to
major food companies. She
specializes in food styling,
recipe testing, cookbook
production and consumer
food product presentations.

Canada
metric

Canadian Food Service
Executives Association
Toronto Branch

Hullah, Evelyn
    Cardinal's Handbook of Recipe Development

Bibliography: p.
Includes index.
ISBN 0-920451-00-4

1. Cookery. 2. Food – Research.
I. Cardinal Kitchens (Firm). II. Title. III. Title: Handbook
of recipe development

TX643.H84 1984   641.5   C84-099233-5

Cardinal Kitchens
Division of
Cardinal Biologicals Ltd.
43 Railside Rd.
Don Mills, Ontario
Canada M3A 3L9

Printed in Toronto, Canada

Preface

Staff home economists of Cardinal Kitchens, experienced in recipe research and development, have long been aware of the limited amount of informative and concise resource literature available on recipe development.

Cardinal Kitchens is the home economics/test kitchen service within Cardinal Biologicals Limited, a Canadian research and development company, prominent in the food industry. Key functions of Cardinal Kitchens are consumer and institutional food product development and testing, recipe development, sensory evaluation and food styling for photography.

This handbook has been published in recognition of the necessity of complete recipe development to supply the consumer, or end user, with appealing and satisfying standardized recipes and the food industry with reliable, consistent recipes tailored to fit specific marketing needs. It provides a valuable Canadian reference for food professionals. The handbook is a comprehensive educational aid for lecturers and students of such fields as home economics, consumer studies, food service management and food product development.

Preparation of Cardinal's Handbook of Recipe Development was made possible, in part, by a federal government grant from Employment and Immigration Canada, Employment Development Branch.

Metric Commission Canada has authorized use of the metric symbol in acknowledgement of metric content and accurate SI usage. Consumer interest has continued for food information that includes both imperial and metric data. This handbook presents material primarily in dual form.

The Canadian Food Service Executives Association, Toronto Branch, endorses this publication as a valuable resource for professionals in food service.

Cardinal's Handbook of Recipe Development is based on information – largely accumulated from the wide experience of our home economists. Cardinal Kitchens' aim is to encourage the establishment and use of guidelines for the whole developmental procedure for recipes. Use of this handbook is instrumental in promoting uniformity, clarity and professionalism in recipe development.

Table of Contents

PART III: RECIPE STYLE GUIDE

PART IV: METRIC RECIPE DEVELOPMENT AND STYLE GUIDE

PART V: RESOURCE INFORMATION

PART VI: SUBSTITUTIONS AND EQUIVALENTS

part I

Recipe Development Planning

A Rationale For Recipe Development

Recipe development is an intriguing and creative process which incorporates sound scientific techniques. It is a systematic progression from initial concept, through information searching, test kitchen trials, evaluations and reformulations, to presentation and writing of final copy. See 'Development of Optimum Recipes', on following page.

In discussions of recipe creative work, both the terms recipe testing and recipe development are used. The distinction in this handbook is as follows:

Recipe development is the entire process of creating from an idea or concept, a unique recipe according to project objectives. Background information is essential to maximize the recipe's potential.

Recipe testing (used in two different senses) is:

1. review, preparation and/or improvement of an existing recipe, or
2. actual, test kitchen preparation of any recipe, whether it be a newly created (development) or an existing recipe (testing).

When recipe testing, the food professional requires limited information about the background and surrounding details of the project.

Since recipe development is more inclusive than recipe testing, this handbook presents material for a complete recipe development process. Recipe testing phases are located in specific sections.

The Food Professional

Food professionals of widely varying backgrounds conduct recipe development. Throughout this handbook, the term home economist is used to describe a person who is actively involved in recipe development. It is freely recognized that other persons instrumental in recipe development include dietitians, chefs, food scientists and food service supervisors. They would apply the same basic approaches, with certain adaptations. Cardinal's viewpoint reflects home economists in business. (For simplicity in text only, we refer to both food professionals and consumer/end users as being feminine).

The role of the home economist is to generate momentum and undertake the responsibility for the whole recipe development process. It is her responsibility to apply food science theory to requested and specific criteria, using her accumulated knowledge and experience in a systematic reproducible way. Her aim is a completely standardized operation. In addition, it is her obligation to represent and reflect consumers' opinion. She is responsible for accentuating features of a specific product; she is an agent or catalyst for increasing product usage via recipe promotion. She is an innovative leader and liaison between the end user (consumer/patient) and management (food company client, institution's administration).

PRODUCT

HOME ECONOMIST

CONSUMER   CLIENT
(manufacturer, agency,
institution, hospital, school)

Development of Optimum Recipes

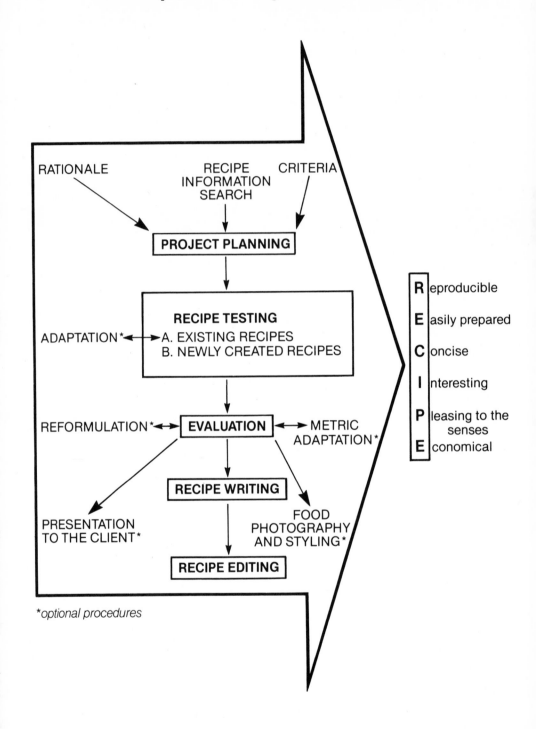

RATIONALE

RECIPE INFORMATION SEARCH

CRITERIA

PROJECT PLANNING

RECIPE TESTING
A. EXISTING RECIPES
B. NEWLY CREATED RECIPES

ADAPTATION*

REFORMULATION*◄► **EVALUATION** ◄► METRIC ADAPTATION*

RECIPE WRITING

PRESENTATION TO THE CLIENT*

FOOD PHOTOGRAPHY AND STYLING*

RECIPE EDITING

R eproducible

E asily prepared

C oncise

I nteresting

P leasing to the senses

E conomical

*optional procedures

Food professionals aim to produce appealing recipes which are accurate and straightforward. Basic management and design principles are applied, as well as adherence to budgets, projected time frames and available printing space. Ultimately, the food professional is challenged to merge scientific, technical and creative skills to produce well-developed recipes which effectively meet project objectives.

Recipe Characteristics

A recipe itself goes far beyond the dictionary definition of a list of materials and directions for preparing a dish or drink; it is a positive combination of sensory qualities which a person will anticipate, enjoy and remember with pleasure. As a total blueprint or pattern, it can be repeated consistently and saved. A recipe has a particular format, title, list of ingredients, series of method statements, yield notation, augmented with additional information.

A recipe is more than the sum total of its parts – it is a mixture of important positive recipe characteristics. A well-developed recipe is:

REPRODUCIBLE – is written in such a way that it can be prepared repeatedly with consistent results. The written copy readily relays an accurate perception of the final product.

EASILY PREPARED – involves a minimum of steps in logical sequence to produce appropriate end results – from simple to complex recipes. Ingredients are used in the easiest possible unit of measure.

CONCISE – is brief without sacrificing clarity.

INTERESTING – has overall general appeal, offers a certain uniqueness and ideally, has beneficial nutrient content. It adds variety to the meal/menu.

PLEASING TO THE SENSES – has stimulating and satisfying flavour and aroma, with appropriate texture and mouthfeel. It is visually appealing to eat or look at. The recipe copy is also stimulating.

ECONOMICAL – has qualities of economy – not always from a budget standpoint, but also economy of human and material resources. Minimum and efficient human energy expenditure, use of dishes, utensils and appliances are appropriate.

Standardized recipes, those which can be clearly understood as reliable and can be repeated under varying conditions with consistent results, are the goal.

Functions Of Well-Developed Recipes

Well-developed recipes serve a number of functions, often overlapping, dependent on whether development has been initiated to:
- increase product usage – advertising and promotion;
- facilitate standardized food service;
- provide meal/menu variety; or
- feature food and equipment.

i. Increase Product Usage

Historically, a manufacturer maintained brand-loyalty through advertising and special services. However, increased competition has infringed upon the traditional market share, causing rapid acceleration of a product's life cycle. This situation has pressured firms to develop new products, modify existing ones or discover new uses for established products.

Specific promotion is required to boost acceptance of most new products – to create consumer demand. Potential customers must realize the existence, advantages and uses of the new product. Continual promotion is required, throughout the product's life cycle.

To expand the use of existing products, food companies are making innovations in flavouring, colouring, packaging and distribution. Consumer approval, reflected in buying practices, determines the success of these modified products.

In this environment, clients request home economists to develop more and more promotional recipes. Frequently used as a major marketing tool, these recipes are designed to increase consumption or utilization of the product. Certain recipes used in marketing programs are legally defined as advertising and in addition must meet pertinent government guidelines.

A recipe's worth as a marketing tool is related to its influence on consumers' attitudes. These are determined by previous experiences with a product, exposure to attitudes of others or promotion. Since positive attitudes lead to positive purchasing action, problems may arise if standards of completeness, reliability and accuracy in recipes are not met. Negative attitudes can result in a loss of time, money and effort for the food company.

A successful product launch requires a great deal of promotional support. Typical recipe promotions appear on packages, savings coupons, written or televised commercials or in product information booklets. To maximize correct product usage, proper preparation steps and recipe suggestions must be available to the consumer.
A new product correctly presented has positive spin-off effects for companion products, increasing overall company sales.

ii. Facilitate Standardized Food Service

Recipes, portions, kitchen techniques, equipment, training and purchasing procedures are each standardized in a food service operation that consistently achieves a quality product. Thorough recipe development ensures that a recipe is standardized and a customer receives an identical product each time. Consistent recipe results are obtained regardless of when the recipe is prepared or who prepares it. Management is then better able to control both quality and costs.

iii. Add Menu/Meal Variety

In homes, institutions or food service operations, there is a continual demand for new and appealing recipes which use traditional foods, introduce new foods or demonstrate popular cooking methods and equipment. Recipes present opportunities for seasonal or theme dishes to add variety and interest to menus or menu rotation. Improved nutrition or conscious diet choices are possible additional benefits.

iv. Feature Food and Equipment

An extension of promotional recipe development is the use of recipes to emphasize particular features or assets of individual foods. Articles discussing foods have more meaning if accompanied by practical recipe ideas. An example of a food's use is more effective than a wordy explanation.

Ideas or points of view are emphasized or made more interesting or memorable if accompanied by recipes. For example, information on how a local food product can be prepared, cooked, served, preserved or frozen in a variety of ways, is well received by both producers and consumers. Likewise, recipe ideas increase acceptance and encourage use of microwave ovens or other new equipment.

Standardization of Recipe Development

Standardization is the optimum goal for a recipe development procedure. THE IMPORTANCE OF COMPLETENESS, ACCURACY AND RELIABILITY IN RECIPE DEVELOPMENT CANNOT BE OVEREMPHASIZED, whether developing recipes for consumers, patients or other end users. Too often, shortcuts are taken – resulting in unreliable disappointing recipes. The importance of techniques of standardization has been acknowledged widely within certain segments of the food industry and should continue to be encouraged.

Acceptance and implementation of standardized techniques and guidelines have widespread continuing benefits for both clients/management and the food professional.

Standardization of recipe development gives further credibility to the value of the traditional home economics discipline. As the importance of proper recipe development is continuously emphasized, the much needed and skilled service of the home economist will be strengthened.

B Project Planning

Before starting a recipe development project, it is necessary to develop a written project plan. Progressive stages in recipe development are thoroughly outlined in the following chapters; however, success in carrying these out is dependent upon applying organizational skills. An objective approach to project planning will produce dividends in efficiency and satisfaction.

To develop a project plan, one must first understand a project's purpose and priorities. Steps required to meet that purpose can be determined, evaluated and worked into a logical flow. Available resources (e.g. manpower, kitchen facilities, time and budget allocation) have a direct influence on the project plan.

All projects take place in an environment composed of a variety of interrelated, constantly changing human (mental) and physical factors, each of which affects various project phases.

In recipe development as elsewhere, shortcuts may curb costs but add risk to attaining success. Action steps may indicate obvious ways to save time and increase efficiency by combining or overlapping steps. For example, multiple recipe testing may be conducted in parallel stages or testing may be combined with visual, verbal or written evaluation.

List-making may prove useful in putting thoughts and plans on paper. Recording ideas can save time and energy later. New projects may begin by revising an old list. Use of time-flow graphs, plan of action charts and standardized forms can supplement or replace itemized lists. Such tools help people to:
- evaluate priorities and objectives
- see action steps more clearly in sequence
- include all tasks
- organize and reorganize, allotting time appropriately
- judge physical environment factors
- communicate with others
- provide motivation and a sense of accomplishment
- record for future reference and/or evaluation.

The "Project Planning Pattern" chart, on the following page, illustrates the central project plan phases, as well as the interacting influences of resources (human, physical, time and monetary).

Project Planning Pattern

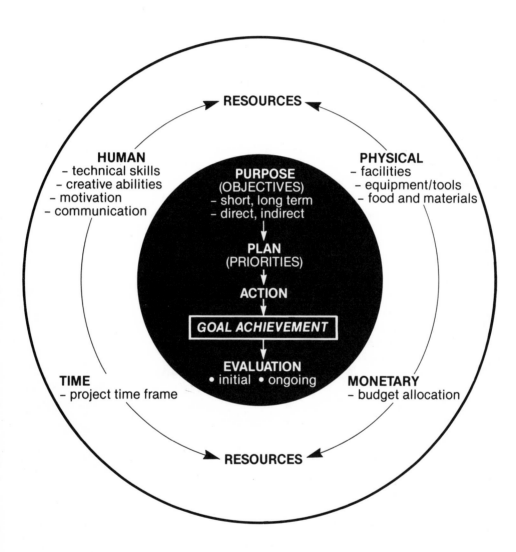

C Identification Of Recipe Project Criteria

Certain criteria are identified before actual recipe development is undertaken. Appropriate criteria for a recipe choice are pinpointed through discussions with the client*, in order to define:
1. the client's project objectives;
2. background information on the client;
3. background information on the product; and
4. the consumer/end user.

1. Client's Project Objectives

To clearly establish the purpose of the recipe(s) – to learn what the client plans – the client and home economist must discuss a series of questions and options. Whether examined in a formal or informal manner, it will be of prime importance to consider the following:

- **HOW** will the recipe be used? Will it become part of a promotional campaign? Will it become part of a collection of recipes designed to meet a particular need? (e.g. recipes for the diabetic.)
- Is the recipe being developed to introduce a **NEW** product or to feature new or extended uses for an **ESTABLISHED** product?
- **WHERE** will the recipe be used? Will it be featured nationally or geared towards a particular market segment? (e.g. Quebec, Maritimes, Western.)
- Have **PREVIOUS SIMILAR PROJECTS** been undertaken? If so, what was particularly successful or disappointing and why?
- How **PROMINENT** should the client's product be in the recipe? Will the recipe involve **TIE-IN** products? If so, how central are they?
- Is the recipe to be an **ADAPTATION** or **NEW** version of an old established recipe?
- Are there any existing **SPECIFICATIONS** regarding the number of recipes to be developed for a series?
- Is the recipe targeted for a **PARTICULAR SEASON,** (climate, holiday or event)?
- Are there guidelines or restrictions as to **THEME** or **CATEGORY** (categories) for the recipe(s)? (e.g. quick and easy, gourmet, everyday, low calorie, budget meal, menu placement.)
- Will the recipe be tested with **COMPETITORS' PRODUCTS**?
- Will consideration be given to **PHOTOGRAPHING** or **FILMING** the completed recipe?
- What recipe **FORMAT** is preferred? Are there any restrictions in terms of length, space, etc.?
- What are the proposed **TIME SCHEDULES** for the project?
- What is the total **BUDGET** or budget allotments for the project?
- Who is the home economist's **DIRECT CONTACT**?

2. Client Information

Although the nature of each project varies, it is an asset to know the institution's or company's business, its general priorities and its objectives related to the product involved. Home economics resources may be available within the client's organization (including branch or associate companies). Relevant lines of authority and responsibility for the project are equally important.

If samples of previous recipes or recipe development work are available, a general assessment of these will prove useful. Pertinent results of market surveys or analysis regarding the product also give worthwhile background.

3. Product Information

For further assessment of the product(s), specific data should be acquired. This information may be obtained from:

    i. the product manager or section representative;
    ii. on-staff home economists;
    iii. available technical research; or
    iv. personal research.

Questions regarding the product data include:

- Is the product for a **GROCERY/RETAIL** or **FOOD SERVICE** market?
- What are the **SPECIAL FEATURES** of the product to highlight? (e.g. low calorie, convenience, gourmet.)
- What are **CURRENT USES** of the product?
- Does the product have one **DOMINANT FLAVOUR** which is best combined with certain foods, spices, herbs, etc.? Is the product flavourless and therefore, suitable for combination with a wide variety of foods?
- What are the significant physical **PROPERTIES** or technical data associated with the product?
  I. Is **STABILITY** affected if the product is, or is not, combined with certain foods (e.g. whipping cream with sugar)? Can the product stand at room temperature for extended periods of time? Will high temperatures or humidity alter the product?
  II. Does the product need to be **STORED** under certain **CONDITIONS** (e.g. cool, dry place)? Will it absorb odours? What is the product's shelf life?
- Are specific **PREPARATION STEPS** required for the product? Should the method be modified, due to outdated procedures or product reformulations? Can the product be prepared in advance, then refrigerated?
- Does the product require the use of **SPECIALIZED COOKING EQUIPMENT**? (e.g. a microwave oven, food processor.)

4. The Consumer/End User

While researching the objectives and background of the project, the professional also defines the typical consumer who will ultimately use the recipe. Specialized products are generally attractive to only certain segments of the population. Certain factors which may influence recipe choice are explored:

- Will all **AGE CATEGORIES** find the product appealing or is it focused on particular groups, such as children or teenagers? (See Part I Appendix, Reference a.) Are certain age groups more familiar with the product's use and versatility?
- Can people of all **INCOME BRACKETS** use the product or due to its price, is it considered by some, a luxury? (Reference b.)
- Will **SINGLE PERSONS** as well as large **FAMILIES** use the product or does it appeal to one specific category?
- Does the **POPULATION WORKING OUTSIDE THE HOME** find the product appealing due to its convenience features? Is it quick and easy to prepare? (Reference c.)
- Will only **ESTABLISHED USERS** of similar products find the product geared towards them or does it attract **NEW USERS** as well?

- Could **CHILDREN** or less knowledgeable cooks easily prepare the product or does it require more cooking expertise?
- Will specific **ETHNIC GROUPS** be more attracted to the product or is it used by persons of all cultures and religions? (Reference d.)
- Do consumers who live in a particular **GEOGRAPHIC LOCATION** use the product more frequently than those in other locations? (Reference e.)

To stimulate general increase in consumer satisfaction with recipes, it is not sufficient to define the consumer in terms of demographics only. The consumer's concerns regarding cooking and recipes must also be considered as they may influence a recipe's effectiveness or acceptance.

In a report by the Benjamin Company Inc. (1980), it was found consumers raised requests in the following order of importance:

a. **Good Nutrition** – recipes which use foods in their natural form without preservatives, contain preparation methods which preserve nutrients and involve proper food combinations which contribute to optimum nutrition.

b. **Quick and Easy Recipes** – recipes which can be prepared in advance, recipes with less steps, cooking with convenience foods and easy-to-locate ingredients.

c. **Economical Cooking** – the use of cheaper cuts of meats, in particular.

d. **Back-to-Basics** – a trend back to cooking from scratch – also decrease in the use of sweets, gravies, sugars, fats and salt; more emphasis placed on the basic food groups.

e. **Appliances** – proper instruction on the uses of the product.

f. **Preservatives** – the use of additive-free foods.

g. **Vegetables and Fruits** – greater concentration on vegetables of all kinds.

h. **Microwave** – more microwave recipes.

i. **Calorie Count** – calorie count included with recipes.

j. **Natural Foods** – more bulk, fibre, meat substitutes and protein alternatives, with less processed foods.

k. **The Working Cook** – meals which were fast, easy and nutritious.

l. **Substitutions** – listing alternate ingredients – major interest in spices and herbs.

m. **Gourmet/Specialty Foods** – desire for specialty recipes.

n. **Other** interests that could be grouped under various headings included leftovers; servings for one or two; packaging and advertising; storage; international/ethnic foods; metrics; meat consumption; and special dietary needs.

A further study by L.D. Gibson (1981), also considered consumer satisfaction with recipes. The specific characteristics of nutrition, expense, taste and effort involved in a recipe were surveyed to determine their contribution to consumer satisfaction. It was found, nutrition and expense each made up about one-third of total food satisfaction; taste and work involved, each contributed about one-fifth.

Unfortunately, it was found that homemaker satisfaction was inversely related to the importance of each characteristic. About one-half of the homemakers reported they were at the level they wanted to be on for the work characteristic, while only one-third were where they wanted to be on taste. Approximately one-fourth felt they were at the right level of satisfaction on expense. On the health characteristic, only about one-fifth were satisfied.

There is the unavoidable fact that by emphasizing the optimization of one characteristic, dissatisfaction may build in others. All characteristics are important to some degree. For example, the consumer preparing a stew may substitute frozen vegetables for fresh ones, simply because there is less effort and expense involved. But, the consumer may be willing to prepare fresh vegetables because she feels they are more nutritious or better tasting.

Where the needs or attitudes of a particular target group are not completely understood, established sources should be researched. Market surveys may be studied or direct input from a company's marketing department may be beneficial. More information on nutritional requirements or food preferences of particular groups such as infants, the elderly, pregnant women or the handicapped may be pertinent.

Keeping the end user's wants and needs in the forefront is essential when establishing criteria on which to develop recipes. It must be noted, that these expressed needs and desires change rapidly; therefore, if the information is to be of value it must be current.

As each of the many interrelated factors are considered, a clearer picture of the recipe requirements is visualized.

A checklist approach may be helpful to pinpoint aspects involved in identification of criteria for recipe development. A model is presented in Part I Appendix.

The term client refers to marketing representatives from the food industry and management in food service.

D Recipe Information Search

The recipe information search is the stage of testing and development in which sources for various recipes and recipe ideas are reviewed. This "desk-work" phase provides the opportunity to apply personal knowledge and experience with material already written or accumulated.

Where To Search

Recipe search could be an interesting yet unending process if not controlled within the project objectives. Time constraints are balanced with the need to use as many possible resources as feasible. Material resources including cookbooks, magazines, textbooks, newspaper food pages, libraries, indexes, previous project files for the client, company brochures and pamphlets are the obvious starting point. A computer data base may be accessible. These searches often direct other sourcing or stimulate resourcefulness.

A straightforward idea search through a supermarket may spark ideas, as may a trip to ethnic, gourmet or specialty shops. Imagine the typical eventual consumer and keep her lifestyle in mind. She is exposed to, or is searching for recipes that are appetizing, imaginative, fun, yet practical and nutritious. Visualize purchases, preparation, cooking and eating of the food – each with its possible pleasures and problems.

Human resources are always key in any project. Incorporate ideas from your own accumulated experience, thoughts, impressions – also family, associate and peer-contact behaviour. Resource people such as marketing board representatives, corporate home economists and government agency technical representatives can be very helpful.

Brainstorming, either alone or with co-workers, produces fresh ideas and is a good experience from which to separate far-fetched ideas, develop potential ones and combine or restructure existing ideas.

How To Search

Using the previously discussed list of appropriate, specific recipe characteristics, compile actual printed recipes in a traditional or computer file. A recipe collected from one of these sources is intended to be a starting inspiration or idea only – requiring many changes, or complete redirection, in most cases. Changes or variations in method statements, cooking techniques, quantity sizes, measure system or recipe format may be necessary. In many cases, a substitution of at least one ingredient may be considered. Possibly an exotic ingredient could be replaced with a more readily available one, or vice versa.

Even if only a few characteristics are appealing for the purpose of the project, the ideas should be saved to be incorporated with other partially developed ideas.

Food Preparation Theory

Incorporated with the review of general positive recipe characteristics (see Rationale for Recipe Development), is a need to apply basic food preparation theory and food science knowledge. Familiarity with the theory that applies to the recipe being planned is very important and basic text review may be necessary to understand the related principles. For example, prior to development of new product uses for gelatine, the food professional will need to know that the formulation of a gel requires the three steps – separation of the gelatine granules either by mixing with sugar or sprinkling over cold water, dissolving in a sufficient quantity of hot liquid and stirring until dissolved.

To ensure control over consecutive recipe trials, it is important to be knowledgeable as to how a change in either ingredient or method will generally affect the end results. Formulae, conversion factors, ingredients and methods are all researched. Without this knowledge, the whole process of recipe testing and development becomes a costly, haphazard "trial and error" exercise.

Application of food science theory to a specific product recipe allows for the opportunity of capturing interesting features inherent to the physical properties of the ingredient. For example, mixtures including ingredients of two different densities could lead to a very appealing effect of a two-layer look in a finished product.

Adapting Material For Project Use

Invariably, material collected from:
- existing recipe copy;
- general professional knowledge and experience; and
- application of food preparation theory

cannot be automatically assembled to create instant end results. Adaptation is usually essential to develop the customized results intended.

All possible recipe ideas have been accumulated in the initial stages of the recipe information search. Whether for one recipe or a series, quick, efficient scanning or review of material with comparative recipe characteristics is desirable.

Careful consideration should be given to the photographic potential of the recipe, if this phase is included in the project outline.

From the many items sourced, choices are made to decide which recipe(s) to proceed with in the actual test kitchen work. Careful review at this stage helps to ensure that time-consuming recipe testing is not uselessly carried out. On the other hand, ideas which are in written form are sometimes difficult to judge from a sensory standpoint. Appeal to the senses is a **KEY** factor in a recipe's success; thus potentially interesting taste combinations should not be overlooked.

The issue of adapting material implies that recipes are based on already existing copy. Over the years, classic recipes have been passed from one person to another, with old favourite combinations appearing time and time again. However, it is unacceptable to simply use an existing recipe, for promotion and imply that it is original – except in certain cases of application of basic resource material. In the same way that written material is copyrighted, promotional recipes can be considered plagiarized if not changed from the available version. Generally, a recipe is altered in at least three significant ways before it is remarketed. Individual project goals will sometimes dictate even greater care in making sure the recipe is as unique as possible. This is one of the challenges which inspires food professionals to explore new flavouring ideas, cooking techniques and serving suggestions.

The following chart summarizes the 'Recipe Information Search'.

Recipe Information Search

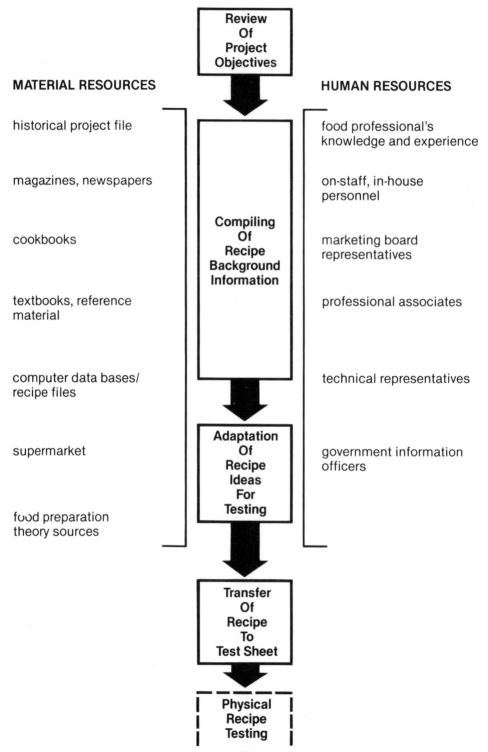

MATERIAL RESOURCES

HUMAN RESOURCES

Review Of Project Objectives

historical project file

food professional's knowledge and experience

magazines, newspapers

on-staff, in-house personnel

Compiling Of Recipe Background Information

cookbooks

marketing board representatives

textbooks, reference material

professional associates

computer data bases/ recipe files

technical representatives

Adaptation Of Recipe Ideas For Testing

supermarket

government information officers

food preparation theory sources

Transfer Of Recipe To Test Sheet

Physical Recipe Testing

15

E Appendix

Appendix 1:

Project #	Criteria Checklist For Recipe Development	Date

_____   _____

Defining The Client's Project Objectives
Discuss these points:
_____ The use of the recipe
_____ New product or new uses of established product
_____ Where the recipe will be used
_____ Outcome of previous similar projects
_____ Prominence of the product or tie-in products in recipe
_____ Adaptation or new version of old recipe
_____ Specifications regarding recipe numbers or series
_____ Particular target regarding season (climate, holiday, etc.), theme or category
of recipe
_____ Testing with competitor's products
_____ Photography or filming
_____ Recipe format
_____ Time schedules
_____ Budget
_____ Contact person

Client Information
Obtain background material:
_____ Knowledge of company's business
_____ Company's priorities and objectives
_____ Related home economics resources
_____ Project authority and responsibility
_____ Recipe development samples and assessment
_____ Pertinent market surveys and analysis

Product Information
Compile data:
_____ Grocery/retail or food service market
_____ Special features of the product
_____ Current uses
_____ Characteristic product flavours
_____ Physical properties or technical data (stability, storage requirements)
_____ Preparation procedures or modifications
_____ Specialized cooking equipment

Defining The Consumer

Explore definitions of the typical consumer of the product:

____ Age category
____ Income bracket
____ Single persons or family units
____ Working/non-working
____ New or established user
____ Levels of cooking expertise
____ Ethnic/cultural/religious background
____ Geographical location

Consider consumer's concerns for recipes:

____ Good nutrition
____ Quick and easy recipes
____ Economical cooking
____ Back-to-basics
____ Appliances
____ Preservatives
____ Vegetables and fruits
____ Microwave
____ Calorie count
____ Natural foods
____ The working cook
____ Substitutions
____ Gourmet/specialty foods
____ Leftovers; servings for one or two; packaging and advertising; storage; international/ethnic foods; metrics; meat consumption; and special dietary needs.

Appendix 2: References* – Recipe Project Criteria

When broadly applied to defining the consumer, the following additional information is relevant.

a. Median age of Canadians will continue to rise as "baby boomers" grow older. In the 1990s the median age will be about 35, which is 10 years older than during the 1960s.

b. Since 1971, there has been a rise in gross family income. In 1980, average family income was $26,610 as compared to $10,368, an increase of 157 percent. However, in real terms over the nine year period, real average family income has increased at an annual rate of 2.2 percent. (The term "family" is used because consumer budget studies suggest that most consumers spend their incomes as part of a family or household unit.)

A 1978 Statistics Canada study of family expenditures reports that households with incomes under $6,000 spent 25.9 percent on food, those with incomes of $16-19,000 spent 17.8 percent, while households with incomes of $35,000 and over, spent 12.9 percent. Therefore, although families earning a higher income spend more money on food, the percentage spent, decreases.

c. In 1965 only 25 percent of wives worked outside the home. By 1978, Statistics Canada reported that full-time working wives were to be found in 39 percent of all spending units and part-time working wives in another 24 percent.

In families where the wife worked, the median income was over 27 percent higher than families with nonworking wives.

A study by the U.S. Department of Agriculture showed that while nutritive value did not suffer, working wives spent more for food and chose more expensive types of food. (This was true in absolute terms, but in percentage terms, the working wife spent less.)

d. More than one-fourth (28.7 percent) of Canada's total population has a French ethnic background.

Studies show French speaking Canadian women as compared to English speaking Canadian women are:

– more oriented towards home, family, children and the kitchen;
– more interested in baking and cooking and more negative towards convenience foods;
– less price conscious; and
– much more concerned about consumer issues.

In the 1970s, about one-quarter of Canada's population were of neither British nor French descent.

e. Since Ontario and Quebec contain slightly more than three-fifths of Canada's total population and account for the majority of consumer expenditures and income, their marketing dimensions are absolutely basic to any national marketing strategy.

The majority of Canadians live within 160 km (100 miles) of the U.S. border.

In 1976, 76 percent of the Canadian population lived in urban areas. Forecasts predict the figure will remain the same in future years. Of the population living in urban areas in 1976, 72 percent lived in suburbs as compared to 51 percent in 1961.

In 1981, percentages of our Canadian population living in the various provinces were:

Ontario and Quebec	–	62 percent	Atlantic Provinces – 9 percent	
British Columbia, the Yukon and Northwest Territories	–	12 percent	Alberta – 9 percent	
			Manitoba and Saskatchewan – 8 percent	

*Based on figures from Basic Marketing (3rd Canadian ed.), McCarthy, E. Jerome and Stanley J. Shapiro.

F Summary

Rationale for Recipe Development

Recipe development is a systematic progression – from initial concept to presentation and writing recipe copy – according to project objectives.

Each recipe should be reproducible, easily prepared, concise, interesting, pleasing to the senses and economical.

Well-developed recipes can increase product usage, provide menu/meal variety, standardize food service and/or be used to feature food and equipment.

Acceptance and implementation of standardized techniques will ensure that completeness, accuracy and reliability in recipes are not overlooked.

Project Planning

A necessary starting point is to develop a written project plan which reflects an understanding of the project's purpose and priorities.

The environment has constantly changing human (mental) and physical factors plus time and monetary limitations. Action steps are implemented to save time and increase efficiency; lists, time-flow graphs, plan of action charts and standardized forms are useful tools.

Identification of Recipe Project Criteria

To develop optimum recipes, the home economist, through discussions with the client, defines:
1. the client's project objectives;
2. background information on the client;
3. background information on the product; and
4. the consumer/end user.

Consumer's concerns regarding cooking and recipes must also be considered as they may influence a recipe's effectiveness or acceptance. Keeping the end user's wants and needs in the forefront is essential when identifying criteria on which to develop recipes.

Recipe Information Search

Utilizing all feasible resources, actual printed recipes and recipe ideas are compiled.

To avoid "trial and error" recipe development and testing, food preparation theory is continually applied and reviewed. Collected recipes or recipe ideas are carefully assessed to avoid expensive, unnecessary testing.

Once specific recipes are chosen for testing, the home economist makes sure the recipes are unique.

part II

Recipe Development Implementation

A Recipe Testing Procedures

The key to maintaining and strengthening the food professionals' standards is thorough testing of all recipes being developed. The home economist has the responsibility to produce absolutely "foolproof" recipes. A consumer needs to be able to follow recipe directions and reproduce, the first time, a successful end product. No part of the recipe, from ingredient choice to method details, should be open for misinterpretation.

The amount of recipe testing required depends on such factors as:

1. project objectives;
2. complexity and characteristics of product and recipe.
3. scope and importance of the recipe usage – e.g. a print ad featuring one particular recipe for a national campaign would require extensive testing;
4. extent to which written plans are valid and proposed tests are successful – related to skills and experience of the home economist; and
5. type of recipe – accuracy is crucial in the development of quantity recipes, mistakes result in a large waste of money, ingredients and energy.

Some ideas work well immediately, while others require modifications and adjustments. Home economists objectively assess results and continue testing until desired results are obtained. If a recipe has an unacceptable flavour, possibly caused by a particular seasoning, it is incorrect to assume that eliminating the seasoning will result in acceptable flavour – the recipe requires retesting.

Recipe testing, like research involves successes and failures in discovering the ideal, acceptable recipe. Unlike the home cook, the professional recipe developer tracks and records ALL creative efforts to ensure that end products can be repeated. Like any scientific experiment, tests need to be confirmed to eliminate chance results. Triple testing of recipes reduces the probability of error caused by chance factors. Final results from triple testing confirm correctness of previous trials. The value of triple testing is shown as follows:

(Note the changes in volume yield throughout the test series.)

Yield Variation Possibilities With And Without Triple Testing

	Yield Results		
	Example A	Example B	Example C*
	L	L	L
TEST 1	1.3	1.3	1.3
TEST 2	1.5	1.5	1.5
AVERAGE OF TESTS 1 & 2	1.4	1.4	1.4
TEST 3 (Triplicate Test)	not completed	1.4	1.6
YIELD AVERAGE VALUE OF TESTED SAMPLES	1.4	1.4	1.5
COMMENTS	– assumed – guesswork – low confidence in results	– Test 3 confirms that first two yields reflected true average – confirms relative consistency of yields – relatively high confidence in results	– Test 3 shows that first two yields did not reflect true average – assumed average after two tests was low by about 100 mL

*Wide span of yields (in proportion to total volumes) indicates need for further attention and testing. Likewise, yield results may have assumed average after two tests was high by about 100 mL.

Recipe Testing Implementation

1. Estimate recipe preparation time and plan to prepare and evaluate a number of recipes during the same time period. Aim to utilize people, time and facilities to the optimum. Plan time schedules carefully to interrelate multiple project steps or testing opportunities, as long as this can be done without jeopardizing accurate results.
2. Consider the most efficient order of work to avoid using extra bowls, cups, measuring tools, extra beating, etc. Keep in mind preparation and cooking techniques that avoid potential circumstances for accidents, injuries or inadequate sanitary practices.
    The choice of size and type of equipment such as knives, skillets or food processors should be appropriate to the type and quantity of ingredients.
3. Never compromise on essentials of safe food handling for the sake of recipe preparation.
4. Consider appropriate pans or containers for the recipe. For example, which pan is the most suitable heat conductor – copper or glass? How will the pan's dimensions, gauge or finish affect the recipe performance? All equipment used should be the standard type that end users/target market group would own.
5. Complete a test sheet for each recipe to be evaluated. Appendix 1 offers an example. Record recipe source, plus other pertinent information. Be thorough when chronicling

this information; this is the central recording sheet for each project recipe. Attach the original recipe (if applicable), which will be helpful during editing.

6. Make an orderly list of ingredients required. All ingredients should be of high quality and readily available brand name items appropriate to the target users. Record on the test sheet, quantities, accurate product descriptions and brand names of all significant ingredients.

7. Assemble ingredients, equipment and utensils. Non-perishable items may be assembled prior to preparation. Note on the test sheet any alteration to equipment or ingredients. Record imperial or metric sizes of cans, containers and packages used. It is much easier to do this minor task as the testing takes place, rather than try to re-source packaging at the copy writing stage.

8. Measure ingredients accurately, making sure to read them on the level. Use simplest possible measure rather than a combination of measures, to avoid possible inaccuracy.

9. Prepare the recipe exactly ACCORDING TO INSTRUCTIONS. Make note of preparation techniques, ease of preparation and exact cooking times. Write on the test sheet, the date of preparation, as well as person(s) involved. Record the size and volume of pans, casserole dishes or other cookware/bakeware required.

10. Some taste-testing may be undertaken while actually preparing the recipe; however, this should be done sparingly.

11. Determine total yield of the recipe, e.g. 4 L (16 cups), as well as the number of standard sized servings, e.g. 5-250 mL/8 oz. glasses.

    If a casserole is prepared, mark the final volume on the side of the pan and measure the amount required to fill the pan to that point.

    To estimate the number of servings, measure approximate portion sizes prior to evaluation. (See Resource Information – Canada's Food Guide – for recommended serving sizes.) If the recipe is for a prepared drink, fill glasses, note the number of glasses filled and the size of the glass. Record results on the test sheet.

    This procedure is carried out with each trial run if changes in amounts of ingredients have been made.

12. Evaluate the recipe. (See Part II.C – Evaluation and Reformulation.)

13. If the recipe is not satisfactory, start from the beginning and define the difficulties. Make modifications to the recipe method or ingredients that will lead to satisfactory end results.

14. Make the changes and retest. Learning is possible from every mistake.

15. If adapting a recipe to a different yield or to the metric system, it is essential to test the recipe and compare it to the original to ensure the two versions are generally alike. Recipes do not always translate or convert precisely. Retesting will guarantee satisfactory results no matter which version or method is used by the consumer/end user.

    When adapting recipes to metric, testing is undertaken after a satisfactory end point is reached for overall acceptability of the basic traditional recipe. The two recipe versions may have slightly different characteristics, since exact mathematical calculations for measures may require rounding. The traditional and metric recipe should be equally acceptable, but they will not be identical.

B Recipe Adaptation

1. INTRODUCTION

Recipes with a wide variety of adaptations are needed for consumers – including variations in recipe format, design, yield, portion sizes, choice of alternate ingredients, cooking methods, equipment or system of measures.

Systems of measure can involve metric, imperial, British imperial units, volume or weight. Recipe performance can be influenced by the system of measure used – especially when ingredients such as fat or leavening agents are involved. For example, the British imperial units have a 10, rather than eight ounce cup; the corresponding teaspoon and tablespoon equivalents will vary from standard imperial measures. Recipes therefore, cannot merely be converted to a new system of measure, but must be adapted and retested.

The choice of cooking methods has broadened over the last few decades. Besides conventional and top-of-the-stove cookery, microwave, gas, barbecue, convection, slow cookery and pressure cooking alternatives are available. Each cooking method has its own unique characteristics.

This section focuses on four frequently required recipe adaptations:
- varying quantities (portion size, yield);
- microwave cooking;
- convection cooking; and
- slow cookery.

2. VARYING QUANTITIES

The majority of recipes printed in the media are family oriented with a unit size of four or six servings. These yields have traditionally been popular since they suit what is perceived as the family unit. When working with such yields and their corresponding serving sizes, the consumer can generally use whole units of ingredients which involve familiar quantities, easily measured with household measures. Typical yields for these consumer recipes also match household cookware and bakeware. However, occasions commonly arise when recipes are adapted for smaller or extended yield. Increasingly often, recipes are needed providing one or two servings. Greater yields are required for larger than average family units, entertaining and quantity food service.

Recipe adaptation for varying quantities requires choices between quality and quantity of ingredients. Quality choices involve suitability of such items as fresh, canned or frozen ingredients or tender/less tender cuts of meat as they relate to a particular recipe's unit size and cooking method. The shopping list must remain practical to avoid partial use of food or potential loss of food quality due to extended storage or spoilage. Method statements must remain compatible with consumer kitchen facilities and equipment.

Recipe adaptation deals with the following quantity factors:
  i. serving or portion size; or
  ii. number of servings.

i. Serving or Portion Size

The terms "servings" or "portions" are interchangeable in meaning but often applied differently. Servings are given for consumer recipes while portions refer to quantity food service recipes.

Guidelines recommended in Canada's Food Guide are the widely accepted starting point for determining serving or portion sizes. Additional portion sizes compatible with those guidelines are offered in Part V – Canada's Food Guide.

Certain recipes are specifically developed for children, the elderly or certain patients who require servings or portion sizes smaller than the population averages. Specialized adaptation which takes into account daily nutritional requirements of these persons becomes a necessary step for these recipe development projects.

In recipe development, total yield is measured as a step in recipe testing. Yield is calculated by total weight for quantity recipes; records of both weight and volume calculations, if available, are more accurate and useful. Weight need not be determined for liquids, spices or dry ingredients in volumes of 250 mL (1 cup) or less.

Recipe products served with a ladle or scoop state yield as 50, as long as yield in recipe testing measures consistently between 48 and 54 servings. Variations appear if a food is liquid or very thick or if the ladle is filled to the level. Most popular yields for quantity recipes are 24-25, 48-50 and 96-100 portions. For some entrées (especially those with crusty or crumb topping), breads, gelatine, salads, cakes and other desserts, these yields reflect ease of cutting.

Standardized portion sizes go hand in hand with a total standardized recipe. Employees will need to be trained in a standardized manner to serve the exact portion sizes specified. If portions are over-generous, not enough people are served; likewise, if portions are smaller than specified on the recipe, there are resulting leftovers and wastage. In both instances, management realizes a loss of profit. Also, standardized cookware or bakeware sizes are needed, especially for baked dishes in order to obtain the expected yield.

ii. Number of Servings

Recipes for One or Two Persons

Due to the growing percentages of smaller households or singles of all ages living alone, there is an increasing need for recipes catering to specific requirements of those persons. They represent a diverse group; some will be individuals with time, income and facilities to enjoy specialized or gourmet cooking; others, perhaps senior citizens, may have limited resources, health problems and a lower overall food intake. Persons on long term special diets (e.g. sodium, fat-restricted) also seek appealing practical recipes.

Smaller recipe yields draw special attention to pre-planning, marketing and alternate storage or cooking methods. Often, smaller quantities relate to smaller scale specialty cookware or bakeware. Popular choices are the recipes which can be varied in different ways or successfully refrigerated or frozen and later served as attractive leftovers. Alternate cooking methods such as "en brochette" provide additional variety. Prepared items may be stored raw to maintain quality features.

Most recipes for four or six servings can be successfully adapted to smaller units by dividing by two, three or four. Units must remain practical as it may be harder to work with smaller measures and there is relatively greater waste from food adhering to pans and spoons. More expensive ingredients could be acceptable when smaller quantities are called for.

With top-of-the-stove or oven cooking, loss of moisture will be comparatively greater than in larger quantity recipes. An increase in liquid may be essential, especially with cream sauces or meat casseroles. To incorporate whole units of eggs, slightly higher amounts can usually be added. Conversely, small eggs or divided, beaten eggs could be tested. In recipes with yeast or baking powder, test slightly larger quantities in proportion to the full recipe. Recipes that do not require rolling or kneading are easier to handle in small quantities.

Recipes for Entertaining or Large Family Units

Entertaining or festive occasions deserve convenient recipes in 8, 10, 12 or 24 serving sizes. Many dessert recipes give 10 or 12 serving sizes. Easily multiplied versatile recipes are helpful. Large families or group homes need such recipes on a regular basis and most pay close attention to costs and time for preparation.

With these recipes, typical household equipment can present limitations. To produce a manageable meal, the solution may be to combine cooking styles and equipment (e.g. top-of-the-stove, oven, microwave and no-bake). Recipes that can be prepared ahead and refrigerated or frozen are also practical.

Recipe testing may demonstrate that the majority of recipes can be multiplied up to four times without changing ingredient proportions. Beyond that range, ingredient compensation becomes significant. For example, some spices may develop stronger, sharper tastes while the effect of others may be reversed. Less liquid is added because evaporation is decreased. Cooking methods may be adapted as the more mass involved, the longer ingredients take to heat, cook or cool.

Quantity Food Service

Key decisions when adapting recipes for quantity food service are whether recipe copy will give metric or imperial measures, in volume or weight or a combination. Most quantity recipes are initially prepared in metric units with weight and volume equivalents. Guidelines for adaptation of traditional recipes to the metric system are presented in Part IV – Metric Recipe Development and Style Guide.

During recipe development hard conversion of ingredients in quantity recipes may very markedly alter a recipe's success and quality. Soft conversion is necessary to minimize potential inaccuracies in measuring which are significant for the increased amount of ingredients involved.

With weight or volume measure, volume is often used for recipes of 25 portions or less, and weights for recipes greater than 25 portions. Dry ingredients and meat are usually weighted and liquids measured; alternately, spices or all dry ingredients in units under 250 mL (1 cup) can be measured by volume. Volume measure can be taken exclusively (except meat) if scales are not available. Weight is given for food as purchased (A.P.), unless otherwise stated. Edible portion weight is specified as E.P. Food service personnel must take consistent care in measuring ingredients and times accurately.

When adapting consumer recipes for quantity levels, steps often include:
a. Reduction of liquids.
b. Lengthening of some cooking times, e.g. sautéing, stir-frying.
c. Adjustment of herbs and seasonings. Direct multiplication may not be successful. Common measures for 50 serving recipes are:

salt	15 mL
pepper	5 mL
spices	5 - 15 mL
herbs	15 - 25 mL
sauces	25 - 50 mL/serving

d. Attention to unique problems related to food science technology, involving certain ingredients such as eggs and vinegar.

In quantity recipes, it may also be an added challenge to maintain quality features such as vegetables' colour and crispness.

3. MICROWAVE COOKING

Principles of microwave cooking must be understood and appreciated to successfully adapt conventional recipes. In the microwave oven, a magnetron vacuum tube converts electricity into high frequency microwaves which are **REFLECTED** off the oven's walls and floor and **ABSORBED BY THE MOISTURE** in food. Absorbed energy causes food molecules to vibrate rapidly, producing friction and consequently, heat to cook food. A stirrer in most ovens circulates microwaves throughout the oven for more even energy distribution. Because reflected rays penetrate foods in an uneven pattern, adaptation of conventional recipes incorporates specific preparation and cooking techniques.

The following section outlines common alterations to cooking times, equipment, techniques and ingredients to adapt a conventional recipe for the microwave oven.

Cooking Times

Microwave cooking times are generally one-third to one-fourth that of conventional. Times, will vary with the wattage output of each particular microwave oven. Household models are typically 500-650 W whereas commercial ovens as found in a food service operation usually have a higher wattage output.

Foods cooked in ovens with less than 600 W output may require extra cooking time while foods in ovens over 700 W may need less time. The home cook checks food at the suggested cooking time, or a little before, to decide if the food in her particular oven model is ready. A recipe developer checks a typical guide to microwave oven settings.

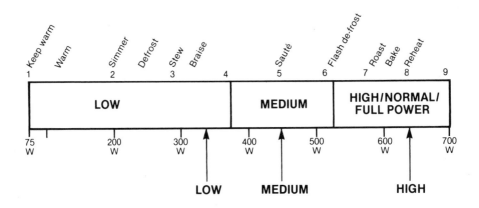

Different oven models use different symbols to denote settings but the above are typical. There is not significant change in microwave cooking time unless the difference in setting is greater than 150 W.

The following table outlines other factors which play a role in determining cooking times:

Factors In Food Which Affect Cooking Time

Cooking Time Increases when Food:	Cooking Time Decreases when Food:
– is greater in weight	– weighs less
– is greater in quantity	– is smaller in quantity
– is greater in volume	(1 serving cooks faster than 6)
– is thick or dense*	– has less volume
– is accompanied with a sauce	– lies flat
– has a cold starting temperature	– is porous in texture
– is of less consistent texture	– contains more moisture
– is greater in height	

*Roasts have high density – bread, low density. Basically, there is little air in high density items therefore, more cooking time is needed.

Standing Times

After microwave cooking, food continues to cook as heat is still being conducted in the food; the temperature of food may still increase up to 16°C (30°F). Standing time allows for evening-up of heat and finishing-off of the cooking process. Generally, 20 percent of the cooking time should be recommended as a standing time prior to serving. Recipes are evaluated after the appropriate standing time has expired. One to three minutes standing time is allowed for small items; up to 15 min for larger ones. Food is covered with lid or foil to keep it hot.

Breakdown Of Total Cooking Time

Time	Microwave Oven
80%	inside
20%	outside (standing time)

Power Levels

Many microwave ovens have at least four power levels – full or high (100 percent wattage output), medium high (70 percent), medium (50 percent) and low (30 percent). High power is recommended in all cases where food quality is not affected, as these levels result in the maximum time saving. Foods with a high moisture content or foods that require fast cooking to retain natural goodness, flavour and texture also require a HIGH setting. Delicate foods such as cream, cheese, eggs, milk, mayonnaise and sour cream require a MEDIUM or LOW setting, since they may toughen, separate or curdle. Less expensive cuts of meat need a LOW setting to aid tenderization. Foods with delicate sauces require a MEDIUM or LOW setting whereas ones with sturdy sauces (tomato, broth or wine) can be cooked on HIGH.

Seasonings

In microwave cooking, there is no external heat to evaporate or change flavours; therefore, it may be necessary to reduce or eliminate certain seasonings or spices, especially salt. Because salt has a tendency to dehydrate and toughen food, it is added to the cooking liquid rather than sprinkled directly on food.

28

Liquids

Since liquids do not evaporate in a microwave oven, they are reduced when converting recipes. There is no specific rule for all recipes, but generally, liquids are reduced by one-third first and then increased if necessary. With soups or stews the liquid should initially be reduced by one-fourth.

Fat

Microwave cooking renders more fat from poultry and meats than conventional methods, so added fat is reduced or eliminated. Added fat is not needed for browning or to prevent sticking. Deep-frying cannot be done in the microwave oven as fats reach a very high temperature. If foods are to be seared, a minimum amount of fat is called for.

Containers/Coverings

Containers are similar in size to the food content, with the exception of liquids or sauces that boil and require a larger container for expansion. Round dishes are preferable. When rectangular dishes are used, foods in the corners become overcooked or dry. Foil shields on the corners will prevent this problem. Generally, a tall, narrow container increases cooking time; a broad, shallow container reduces it. Oven-proof glass, glass ceramic oven dishes or special microwave dishes are best suited to the microwave oven. (See Appendix 2 for suitability of specific dishes and utensils.)

Covers trap steam, speed cooking time and help foods retain their natural moisture. Proper covers include plastic wrap, waxed paper and heat-resistant glass which do not contain metal parts or decorations.

Cooking Techniques

In general, both microwave and conventional cooking utilize the same techniques; however, certain procedures take on greater importance with the microwave oven. To successfully adapt a conventional recipe for microwave cooking, the home economist becomes familiar with these procedures:

i. Stirring

Although a conventional recipe may not require stirring, various foods may need redistribution during microwave cooking time. Microwave ovens usually cook the outside food first; the inside food last. If stirring is incorporated into the recipe it is stated specifically in the method. Stirring is always from the outside in, so the heat is equalized and uncooked portions flow toward the outside edges.

ii. Turning

In the case of large, dense foods (e.g. roasts), turning the food over halfway through cooking will help them to cook evenly.

iii. Rotating

For even distribution and uniform cooking, certain foods (e.g. pies, fish) are rotated one-quarter turn, one or more times during the cooking process.

iv. Arrangement

Pieces of similar foods are arranged in a circular fashion. Potatoes or cupcakes, for example, are placed in a ring shape. Corn-on-the-cob is positioned like the spokes of a wheel. Chicken pieces, chops and other meats which contain bones are spaced so the bony parts face the centre and the thick parts face the oven walls.

Sample Of Recipe Conversion

The home economist, aware of the above factors, is now able to adapt a conventional recipe to microwave cooking. The following recipe illustrates how the required alterations are applied. Once these changes have been incorporated into the recipe copy, the recipe is ready for testing and evaluation. Additional variations are then tested to improve the flavour, texture or cooking method, if necessary.

HUNGRY CHICKEN   Makes 3 Servings

1 kg	2 lb.	chicken, cut-up
25 mL	2 tbsp.	butter ← *reduce*
25 mL	2 tbsp.	oil ← *omit*
250 mL	1 cup	chopped onion
5 mL	1 tsp.	salt ← *omit; add later*
15 mL	1 tbsp.	paprika ← *adds colour*
500 mL	2 cups	vegetable stock or water ← *reduce ¼*
5 mL	1 tsp.	flour
250 mL	1 cup	sour cream — *omit* *omit; add later*

Cook on HIGH for 25 to 45 sec
omit

large glass casserole

Melt butter and oil in a heavy pot. Add onions and brown chicken. Add salt, paprika and stock ... Simmer 1½ hours until tender. Stir flour into... Add to pot slowly. Cook 5 min *add salt to taste*

reduce ¼ – ⅓

Cook on HIGH, turning chicken pieces after halfway point

↑ *casserole (MEDIUM)*

↑ *reduce to 50%*

Other:
– chicken may be skinned to reduce fat

Classification Of Conventional Recipes

The adaptation of conventional recipes to microwave cooking can be classified into the following three categories:
a. easy to adapt;
b. more difficult to adapt; and
c. not recommended to adapt.

Foods which contain significant amounts of moisture are more easily adapted. If cooked conventionally, they would be steamed, poached, stirred or cooked by direct heat (stove-top).

Conventional recipes which are more difficult to adapt involve foods which need extra care (e.g. egg, cream dishes). Certain foods which require browning and crispness fall into this category as they may not always produce the desired result.

It is not recommended to adapt recipes which are prepared by dry heat (white cakes, popovers) or deep-fried or for crisp textured foods (oven-broiled chicken).

a. Easy To Adapt

Examples:

hot dips	bacon
meatballs	Sloppy Joes
meatloaf	pot roasts
less tender meat cuts	stews
casseroles	puddings
scalloped potatoes	hot sandwiches
sauces with flour or cornstarch	jams, jellies
one dish meals with sauces	candies
single foods (especially vegetables)	

b. More Difficult To Adapt

Examples:

cheese/condensed milk dishes	meat appetizers
stir-fried foods	egg dishes
noodle/rice dishes	chicken stew
layered casseroles	fondues
single crust pies	omelettes
egg yolk sauces	quiches
Hollandaise sauce	soups
yeast breads	quick breads
dessert bars	layer cakes
soufflés	pie crusts

c. Not Recommended To Adapt

Food	Reason
Puff pastry, fresh or frozen	puffs in the oven but falls when removed
Turnovers, double crust pies	do not bake on the bottom
Fried appetizers	do not crisp
Biscuits wrapped around sausages	absorb too much moisture from the meat
Hard cheeses	do not melt easily
Deep-fried foods	fat reaches too high a temperature
Oven-broiled chicken	will not have a crisp, browned surface
Fried pork chops	need moisture to tenderize
Whole eggs	will burst
Vegetable casserole layered with bread	bread absorbs moisture from vegetables rather than staying crisp
Pizza	will not have a crisp crust
French bread, hard rolls	do not form a hard crust
Waffles, pancakes	need a hot surface
Cake-style drop cookies	too soft to hold their shape
White cakes	egg whites do not contain enough fat
Popovers, angel, sponge cakes	require dry heat

Factors Affecting Microwave Cookery
In Some Food Categories

When first experimenting with adapting conventional recipes for microwave cooking, the home economist experiences certain common problems. The following list offers potential solutions for these problems.

Foods	Common Problem	Potential Solution
Fruits and vegetables	Certain types do not heat evenly.	Cover dish.
	Certain fruits and vegetables burst.	Pierce skins to stop steam build-up.
Fish and seafood	Whole fish cooks unevenly.	Rotate dish one-quarter turn several times during cooking process.
	Seafood is dry and tough.	Be conservative in cooking times.
Meat	Tender meat becomes tough.	Cook on HIGH power setting.
	Pot roast does not tenderize.	Pierce meat to allow steam from sauce to tenderize.
	Meatloaf is too wet.	Increase dry filler by 125 mL (½ cup) for every 750 g (1½ lb.) of meat. Decrease liquid by ½ if using soft filler.
	Casserole dish lacks flavour and tenderness.	Cover dish.
	Stew is thin, watery or too moist.	Use less liquid.
Poultry	Too much fat.	Remove skin.
	Steam build-up occurs.	Pierce skin.
Meats and poultry	Meat or poultry lacks sufficient colour.	Brush with soy sauce, browning agents, glazes, butter or paprika. To brown further or to crispen skin, place under broiler of conventional oven for five minutes.
	Portions overcook.	Shield thin portions with aluminum foil halfway through cooking. Make sure foil does not touch sides of oven.
Milk products	Coating forms on top.	Do not boil.
	Cheese dishes cook improperly.	Cook on LOW. Fondues and sauces may improve with stirring. Use processed cheese for better melting properties.

Foods	Common Problem	Potential Solution
Pie shells / single crust pies.	Crust is too soggy.	*Cook crust first before adding wet filling.*
	Crust lacks colour.	*Add a few drops of yellow food colouring with the liquid, prior to adding liquid to the flour mixture.*
	Crust shrinks from side of pie plate.	*Prick generously with fork.*
Rice and pastas	Food boils over.	*Add 15 mL (1 tbsp.) cooking oil.*
Sauces and fillings (thickened by starch)	Lumpiness occurs.	*Stir halfway through cooking.*
	Sauce or filling is thin, watery.	*Use slightly less liquid.*
Steamed puddings / cakes	Cake cooks unevenly.	*Use round glass or fluted ring mould. Bake layer cakes one layer at a time. Shield corners of square dishes with triangles of foil. Foil may be removed during last 1½ min of cooking, if necessary.*
	Cakes does not come out of pan easily.	*Line bottom and sides of pan with waxed paper. If waxed paper is cumbersome, line bottom and grease sides of pan. Do not use flour as it bakes onto the surface of the cake.*

Microwave Method Statements

1. In writing a recipe for the microwave oven, the word "microwave" does not mean "cook"; microwave is not a verb.
2. Ideally, the wattage of the oven used to test the recipe, should be stated, e.g.
   Tested in 700 watt microwave oven.
3. State power setting as well as cooking times, e.g.
   Cook 2 min at full power.
   Cover and cook 5 min at medium power.
   Cook at low power until set (5-5½ min).
4. Indicate frequency of required stirring, e.g.
   Cover and cook at full power until vegetables are tender (about 5 min), stirring frequently. Cook milk at low power until scalded (about 5 min), stirring occasionally.
   Cook 3 min at full power, stirring frequently.
5. State whether food is covered or uncovered during standing time, e.g.
   Let stand 5 min (indicates uncovered).
   Let stand, covered, 2 min.
6. When food needs to be rotated state as:
   Rotate cake quarter turn every 2 min or use a turntable.

(See Part III Recipe Style Guide – Method Statement Guidelines for more complete information.)

Microwave Oven Terms

Home economists working with a microwave oven familiarize themselves with some of the terms related specifically to microwave ovens.

CAVITY: The space inside the microwave oven used for cooking.

COMPLEMENTARY COOKING: The combined use of microwave oven and conventional cooking.

MICRO PROCESSOR: The computer control panel on a microwave oven.

MICROPROOF: A term used to refer to cookware or utensils that are safe and recommended for microwave cooking.

MULTI-POWER: A multi-power microwave oven offers selection of many power settings and allows for adjustment to suit food being cooked or to achieve a desired method.

TEMPERATURE PROBE: A special feature on some microwave ovens, the temperature probe enables food to be cooked without the time being set. If the temperature probe is properly inserted and programmed, the oven automatically cooks the food to the preselected temperature.

TURNTABLE: An electrically powered revolving shelf available on some microwave ovens, that helps to equalize cooking.

4. CONVECTION COOKERY

The principle of convection ovens is to broil, roast, bake and braise food by surrounding it on all sides by forced hot air. The air is heated by an element, circulated by a fan, heated and circulated again. Time savings of 20 to 50 percent are realized.

Virtually all foods that can be cooked in conventional ovens can be prepared in convection ovens with very satisfying results. Recipe changes are few, relating mainly to time/temperature settings. As well, convection ovens utilize typical bakeware or no bakeware at all. Standard oven temperatures and times are generally given so the recipes are not restricted to convection cooking.

When adapting recipes for the convection oven, proper testing procedures must be carried out in a standard, commercially available, convection oven.

The following section outlines pointers for adapting conventional recipes for the convection oven.

Baking Guidelines

- Oven temperature is decreased by 15-30°C (25-50°F).
- If a baked item browns sufficiently on the outside before the centre is fully cooked, the temperature is lowered an additional 15°C (25°F), baking time is increased and the recipe retested.
- Time reductions fluctuate depending upon the depth, richness and moisture content of batter or dough. Generally, food will bake in one-fourth to one-third less time.
- To avoid undercooked centres in large items, it is recommended that several small items be baked at the same time. e.g. Split the bread recipe into two small loaves.
- When testing pastry recipes, if the pastry sinks in the centre, the baking time is increased or the temperature raised.
- Exact type of bakeware is specified in the recipe copy; this choice has a direct bearing on the recommended baking time. Metal bakeware produces best results. Aluminum and heavy-duty aluminum foil allow for the greatest time savings. Black steel, cast iron

and enameled cast iron give some time savings. (Glass and flameproof ceramic may be used, but will not necessarily decrease baking time.)

- Whenever possible, the use of a baking sheet with no sides is recommended as this allows for better air circulation and subsequent time savings.
- Baked items are tested with a cake tester to ensure adequate baking.
- The home economist may encounter a baking recipe that will not cook properly because of high moisture or fat content. If lowering the temperature and increasing baking time fails, adjust the recipe by decreasing the liquid, chocolate or cream (or whatever ingredient makes the recipe rich). If this action does not provide suitable results, the recipe may not be adaptable.

Roasting Guidelines

- To convert a standard roasting time, the time is reduced by one-third to begin and then increased as necessary. If meat is brown, but too rare in the centre, lower the temperature and increase time.
- For total browning, tender cuts of meat may be placed directly on the oven rack with a drip pan in place.
- One-eighth to one-quarter inch of water may be added to the drip pan to prevent drippings from evaporating.
- The roast is not covered with aluminum foil as it would increase cooking time.
- Roasts are brushed with glaze or barbecue sauce only during the last 10 to 20 min. Earlier brushing may cause scorching.

Broiling Guidelines

- Standard and convection broiled foods cook in about equal time; convection broiled foods are not turned.
- Recipe copy specifies that the oven is preheated on broil according to oven directions.
- Foods are brushed with glaze or barbecue sauce during last five minutes of broiling.

Adaptation of standard recipe, for convection ovens is illustrated:

ZESTY COMBINATION MEATLOAF   Makes 6 Servings

1 kg	2 lb.	ground beef
125 g	¼ lb.	pork, ground or chopped fine
1	1	large egg
250 mL	1 cup	dry bread crumbs
250 mL	1 cup	milk
125 mL	½ cup	chopped onion
10 mL	2 tsp.	salt
2 mL	½ tsp.	pepper

50 to 60 min

Preheat oven to 180°C (350°F)...Shape into oblong loaf... Place meatloaf on roasting rack in shallow pan. Bake about 1¼ to 1½ h. Serve garnished with watercress.

Place shallow pan below to catch any drippings.

Oven rack and slide into oven so meatloaf is centred. If mixture is too soft to hold its shape on rack, refrigerate loaf 30 min before placing on rack

35

5. SLOW COOKERY

The slow cooker or crock pot, allows the consumer flexibility in meal preparation. Recipes can be prepared early in the day and, after slow cookery techniques, be ready to eat at dinner time.

Foods that benefit from steam heat and extended cooking (such as less-tender, more economical cuts of meat) are ideal. However, not all recipes adapt readily to this method of cooking. Slow cookery operates on the principle of applying slow, even, moist heat; soups, stews and other long cooking meat and vegetable dishes and fruit combinations are best suited.

Assessing a recipe for possible adaptation to slow cookery is the first step. Once a potential recipe is selected, adjustments to ingredients, preparation methods and cooking times are necessary.

Ingredient Guidelines

- Since there is very little evaporation during cooking, the amount of liquid is generally halved when adapting conventional recipes. If pasta or rice is added, more than half the liquid may be required as these ingredients absorb liquid.
- Pasta and rice may become mushy with extended cooking. To avoid this problem, they may be added during the last hour of cooking or cooked separately and stirred in near the end of the cooking time.
- Fresh milk products are not stable when heated for extended periods of time. If a conventional recipe calls for milk, cream or sour cream, substitute evaporated milk or condensed cream soup and add at the beginning of the cooking period. Alternately, milk products can be added at the end of the cooking time.
- Some seasonings, especially salt, are unpredictable when used in a slow cooker. Half the salt is added at the beginning and the rest at the end of the cooking time, if required.
- In a slow cooker many herbs and spices develop a stronger flavour; therefore, the amount needed in conventional recipes is halved. Whole herbs and spices can be removed halfway through the cooking time.

Preparation Guidelines

- A recipe's yield is compared against the capacity of the slow cooker. To function properly the cooker should be at least half full.
- Vegetables such as whole potatoes, carrots and onions cook very slowly and are cut in smaller pieces. Layering vegetables in the cooker's bottom may assist cooking. This placement also allows any meat juices to drip over vegetables enhancing their flavour.
- When a sauce is used, it is poured evenly over the food so that all ingredients cook evenly.

Cooking Time Guidelines

– The following chart illustrates the increased time required to cook recipes in a slow cooker.

Slow Cookery Conversion Time Chart

If Original Recipe Calls For:	Cook On LOW For:	Cook On HIGH For:
¼ - ½ h	4 - 8 h*	1½ - 2½ h
½ - 1 h	6 - 10 h	3 - 4 h
1 - 3 h	8 - 18 h	4 - 6 h
LOW 80°C (190°F) HIGH 150°C (300°F)		

*Most uncooked meat and vegetable combinations will require at least 8 h on LOW.

Certain factors which affect cooking times include:

– Cooking time can be decreased substantially by preheating the liquid. Foods at room temperature cook faster than cold foods.
– Fats tend to increase the cooking temperature; therefore, foods cook faster. To eliminate large amounts of fat, meats are trimmed, browned or broiled prior to cooking.
– Minerals, acids and sugars will increase the cooking time of dried bean products and are added only after the beans have softened.

Evaluation and Reformulation

A recipe should not only be workable in terms of preparation, it must also please the tastes and preferences of a significant group of consumers. It is therefore important to be sure that the texture, appearance and flavour of the prepared dish are appealing. While not every recipe will satisfy everyone, the recipe developer verifies that the recipe is acceptable by critically evaluating the above qualities.

Texture is a significant and often under-rated aspect of food quality – sometimes even more influential than flavour and appearance. As part of a consumer awareness study, it was discovered that texture greatly affected people's image of food. "Laboratory-consumers" felt texture was most important in bland foods and foods that were crunchy and crisp.

Appearance probably has the greatest initial influence on food acceptability as it either succeeds or fails to stimulate appetite. However, once food has been tasted, both colour and texture become secondary to flavour.

Flavour is mentioned by an overwhelming portion of consumers as the reason for overall preference and continued product use. Smoothness, roughness, granularity and viscosity can all affect flavour.

Guidelines for Evaluation

After completing the recipe preparation, it is necessary to thoroughly evaluate the outcome. Ideally, more than one person should assess the recipe. A solitary person may react to personal biases – ones which may not be consistent with general consumer tastes and preferences. As well, the lone evaluator may overlook a significant fault which another person would notice.

One of the most vital aspects of proper assessment is objectivity, whether working alone or with others. Prior to evaluating the finished recipe, aim to set yourself apart from the recipe. Consider the sensory features AFTER detaching yourself and only then, be objective and decide the merits of the recipe.

To assist in making decisions, be aware that the whole range of pertinent recipe factors combine and interact during evaluation. Physical characteristics such as texture are judged along with other factors (e.g. nutrition and cost) as they relate to the project objectives.

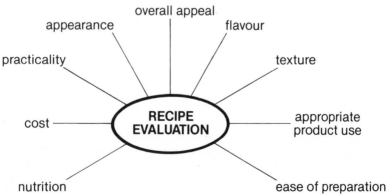

overall appeal
appearance · flavour
practicality · texture
cost — **RECIPE EVALUATION** — appropriate product use
nutrition · ease of preparation

Certain key points are considered for each of these factors and a review of these qualities may prove beneficial. The project's goal or aim is kept clearly in mind when evaluating a recipe.

Recipe Characteristic	Points to Consider
Appearance	– Is overall appearance good? – Can the appearance, form or size be improved by changing the baking or serving dish? – Can the appeal be enhanced by adding a sauce, topping or garnish? – Can the colour or visual texture be improved by adjusting ingredients or the ingredient preparation? – Can the method be varied so certain ingredients are more prominent?
Flavour (odour/taste)	– Is the recipe suitably spicy, salty, tart or sweet? – Do the individual flavours blend or does one ingredient mask the rest? – Is the flavour strength in accord with the purpose of the dish? – Is the odour appealing, nontypical or lacking?
Texture	– Is smoothness, roughness, granularity or viscosity appropriate? – Would altering the texture of one ingredient or introducing a new texture, improve the overall appeal?
Appropriate use of specific product	– Is the product featured adequately? – Is the product subtle enough or consistent with project objectives (e.g. special diet products)? – Is the recipe yielding a dish which is standard in basic characteristics?
Ease of preparation	– Does the ease/difficulty of preparation, number of dishes/appliances used and length of time required meet the project goals? – Can the method be improved to make the recipe simpler, more convenient and less time consuming?
Overall appeal	– Does the recipe look and taste appetizing? – Will the recipe "sound" appealing when read? – If photographed, will the recipe appear inviting?
Practicality	– Are whole units of ingredients used? – Are ingredients readily available? – Does the yield suit the project goals?
Nutrition	– If compatible with client objectives, does the recipe supply meaningful nutritional content? If not, can a garnish or accompaniment increase the nutritional value?
Cost	– Is the cost practical for the type and yield of the recipe?

If part of a larger home economics staff, present the finished recipe to three or four food professionals or experienced panelists. Plates, cutlery and serving utensils need to be available. When a number of recipes are to be evaluated, provide the panel with water and/or crackers. This will eliminate flavours of one recipe carrying over while tasting another.

As the recipe is presented, explain its purpose and use. Make sure each dish is evaluated for individual qualities.

Note on the test sheet any suggested changes. In some cases, minor variations can be tried immediately. Should the panel suggest more spices, sprinkle them onto the prepared recipe and evaluate again. Once a consensus on the spice level is reached, the entire recipe is prepared again and re-evaluated.

If numerous dishes from one project are being assessed, a scoring preference test sheet (Appendix 3) may be helpful. Ensure each recipe is thoroughly evaluated before moving to the next one. Always judge in order of weakest to strongest flavour to ensure the tastebuds are not desensitized.

When evaluation indicates reformulation is required, consideration should be given to the best approach.

Approaches to Reformulation

1. Adjust ingredients/method to better create acceptable product/recipe characteristics. e.g. Altered texture, appropriate use of specific product or ease of preparation.
2. Consider potential variations and substitutions of ingredients. They could be filed for future use, perhaps cross-referenced on a computer.
3. Change the order of method steps. e.g. One ingredient might have lost its substance or flavour due to extended cooking.
4. Vary the preparation technique. e.g. Method originally called for adding all ingredients to base at once, when additional steps would conserve quality characteristics.
5. Consider the cooking method which would be most appropriate. e.g. conventional, microwave or convection. Examine further cooking method modifications e.g. Temperature adjustments, preheating the oven.

Following this, any changes should be incorporated into the recipe formulation and the recipe prepared for a second test and evaluation. All changes are accurately recorded on the original test sheet, or attachment if required.

The above process is repeated until there is complete satisfaction with the recipe.

If a number of recipes are being tested for a series or a cookbook, an updated list of approved recipes should be kept along with a brief description of each. (See Recipe Summary Sheet, Appendix 4.) In this application, variety is the aim, to give an appealing base for the collection.

In summary, objective evaluation will lead to effective judgments on recipe qualities and help to speed the reformulation steps necessary. At this stage, the critical decision is made on final acceptance of the basic recipe. The recipe can now be presented to the client, or written.

D Presenting The Recipe To The Client

After completion of recipe(s) testing, evaluation and reformulation, presentation to the client can be officially conducted. The client will give his personal evaluation of the recipe's flavour, appearance, composition, appeal and suitability in terms of meeting project goals.

Preparation of the Recipe

When preparing the recipe for presentation, it is essential to follow directions exactly. Approach it the same way a consumer would, as if it is the first time you have seen the recipe. This attitude will allow a confirmation that the recipe is truly problem free.

At this stage, ingredients or methods are not added to make the recipe more appealing. Depending on the scope of the project, garnishes may be included or suggested later, but do not rely too heavily on their presence to gain approval. The recipe, itself, is the centre of attention.

Prior To Presentation

Careful consideration of an appropriate method of presentation is warranted. Will the recipe be displayed singly or as part of a plate which depicts a complete meal? Should it be shown as a whole recipe, perhaps in its baking dish, or as one serving portion cut from the whole? If time and budget allows, could one or two variations of the recipe (pie, tarts) or two or more placements in a meal (appetizer, entrée) be illustrated simultaneously?

To accentuate the recipe, the home economist may consider the dishes and utensils used during presentation. Whether suggested or actually used, the serving dish could immediately suggest a particular season, holiday or occasion for new or extended usage. This may be of special importance if the recipe is later to be photographed.

The more usual choice of a basic or nondescript plate (clear, plain white) may highlight the recipe – emphasizing its uniqueness, eye-appeal, colour, texture or dominant ingredient or feature. The dish should be appropriate in size, type and appeal.

Emphasize the recipe and ingredients. The use of an appropriate garnish or small accompanying item may assist, but must remain understated.

If the recipe is potentially difficult to serve (lasagna, pie), the home economist should consider cutting a serving prior to presentation. This preparation will help avoid a possible awkward situation; it will also illustrate the number of portions or serving size.

Serving utensils, plates, cutlery and napkins will be available for the client.

Presentation to the Client

Once the meeting with the client begins, a business-like, organized, uncluttered, quiet environment is an asset. As the recipe is presented, it is briefly outlined. With the test sheet readily available, the home economist can accurately answer questions.

If a series of recipes has been developed, the home economist will indicate how each individual recipe fits into its particular category (e.g. entrée, appetizer). As variety is an essential element of a series, differences in individual recipes are itemized.

When presenting the recipe, the home economist may discover the client disagrees with her ideas. At times, involved discussions take place. Personal preferences, or dislikes, must be controlled to professionally evaluate a recipe.

The home economist must attempt to suppress extraneous biases by firmly presenting the features as fitting the outlined project requirements. She supports her choices and disagrees with any changes she finds inappropriate. Conversely, she does not have a closed mind about the client's negative comments. Company representatives often provide valuable background direction for recipe reformulation. Record all suggested changes so there is a clear understanding of what further action is needed.

After the recipe has been evaluated by the client, the home economist will discuss recipe format if decisions have not previously been reached. Length, the inclusion of optional/alternate ingredients or other variations should be decided.

The home economist may want to initiate discussions on photography if this is included in the project. If a series is involved, the home economist can provide input as to which recipes she thinks will photograph best. She may wish to point out the specific recipes she would choose based on their photographic potential. A separate presentation, specifically with food styling emphasis may be appropriate.

Following Presentation

If the client has suggested changes, the home economist tries to incorporate these into the recipe. The recipe will then be tested again. At times, the home economist may find she goes back to the original recipe files and starts from the beginning.

When the client is satisfied and no further changes are required, final writing of the recipe can proceed.

E Appendix

The following SAMPLE
FORMS offer valuable
material which the home
economist will find instrumental for recording creative
ideas and technical results.
Further development or
modifications may be
required to suit individual
needs.

Appendix 1: Recipe Test Sheet

Product:		Variety:		Requested By:
NAME:		NUMBER:		TESTED BY:

METHOD:

INGREDIENTS:			AMOUNTS:		
Food	Type	Brand	#1 (Date)	#2 (Date)	#3 (Date)
			Yield:	Yield:	Yield:

Comments: Product (Appearance, Flavour – Odour/Taste, Mouthfeel – texture, Other)

#1

#2

#3

Comments: Method

Recipe Tested 1 ( ) 2 ( ) 3 ( )	Recipe Source:	Other:
Approved for presentation ( )		
Date presented:		

44

Appendix 2: Dish and Utensil Safety for Microwave Cooking

Type of Utensils/Dishes	Microwave Safe?	Exceptions
Glassware	yes	*Do not use those with metal trim. Delicate glassware may crack.*
Unglazed, glass, ceramic	yes	*Must not contain metal or plastic parts.*
Glazed, glass, ceramic	no	
Pottery, earthenware, stoneware, fine china/porcelain	*	**Try dish safety test. Place 250 mL (1 cup) water in a separate container that is next to the dish to be tested. Set for 2 min on HIGH. Dish should remain cool or warm to the touch. If dish becomes hot and water remains cool, DO NOT USE THE DISH. If dish is warm, use with caution.*
Plastics	yes (short time)	*High temperatures can distort plastics or can cause leaching of toxic chemicals. Do not use twist ties.*
Paper	yes (short time)	*Plates, towels, napkins, bags with printing or colours should not be used.*
Wood/straw	yes (short time)	*Wood may crack after prolonged use.*
Crystal/cut glass, antique glassware	no	
Foil containers	yes, sparingly (with care)	*Must be high proportion of food to metal. Food must not be enclosed in metal or completely wrapped in foil.*
Metal cookware/bakeware	no	
Rubber	no	
Thermometers	no	*Unless specifically designed for microwave.*

Appendix 3: Scoring Preference Test Sheet

Date _____

Participant _____

Product _____

Evaluate these foods and indicate how much you like or dislike each. Use the number on the 5-point scale that best describes your feeling about each food. The most desirable score is 5; the least desirable is 1. Please give reasons for this attitude.

Desirable ⟶ 5 · 4 · 3 · 2 · 1 · ⟵ Undesirable

Recipe Name/Code	General Appearance	Flavour (Odour/Taste)	Mouthfeel	Ease of Preparation	Common Ingredients	Frequency of Use	Other Comments

Appendix 4: Recipe Summary Sheet

PROJECT: _____   DATE: _____

| Recipe Name | MEAL PLACEMENT | | | | COMPLEXITY | | | COST | | | OCCASION | | | |
	Appetizers	Side Dishes	Entrées	Dessert	Easy	Medium	Complex	Budget	Medium	High	Everyday	Seasonal	Holiday	Entertaining

Summary

Recipe Testing Procedures

To produce absolutely "foolproof" recipes, the home economist objectively assesses results and continues testing until desired quality features are obtained. The amount of testing depends on a number of factors. Triple testing procedures are recommended and reduce the probability of chance. Test sheets provide a central recording page for each recipe project.

If after evaluation the recipe proves unsatisfactory, or it is adapted to a different yield or measuring system, modifications are undertaken and the recipe is retested.

Recipe Adaptation

Varying Quantities

Although most consumer recipes are for four or six servings, recipes are often adapted to smaller (one or two servings), larger (eight to twenty-four servings) or quantity food service proportions. Quality and quantity ingredient factors are taken into account. The second group involves a recipe's serving or portion size and number of servings. Method statements must also remain practical for the appropriate consumer or food service kitchen facilities.

Microwave Cooking

To successfully adapt a conventional recipe, cooking times, equipment, techniques and ingredients are modified.

The adaptation of conventional recipes can be classified into three categories:
a. easy to adapt (foods which contain moisture);
b. more difficult to adapt (foods which require extra care and attention or browning and crispness); and
c. not recommended to adapt (foods which require cooking by dry heat).

The home economist may experience certain common problems when first experimenting with adaptation; however, potential solutions are offered.

Familiarization with certain microwave method statements, oven terms and cookware requirements is helpful.

Convection Cookery

Virtually all foods cooked in a conventional oven can be prepared in a convection oven. Recipe adaptation involves adjustments to time/temperature settings as they relate to baking, roasting and broiling foods.

Slow Cookery

Determination of whether a recipe is suitable for slow cookery is the first step of recipe adaptation. Following that decision, adjustments to ingredients, preparation methods and cooking times are necessary.

Evaluation and Reformulation

Objectivity is a key factor when evaluating the pertinent recipe factors – appearance, flavour (odour, taste), texture, appropriate use of specific product, ease of preparation, overall appeal, practicality, nutrition and cost.

Individual qualities of each recipe are thoroughly evaluated personally, by co-workers or experienced panelists.

If evaluation indicates reformulation, consideration must be given to the best approach. Changes are noted on the original test sheet. A scoring preference test sheet and a recipe summary sheet may also aid the home economist.

Presenting the Recipe to the Client

The client will want to evaluate the recipe's flavour, appearance, composition, appeal and suitability in terms of meeting project goals.

To ensure the recipe is problem free, it must be prepared just as a consumer would.

Appropriate means of presentation are considered – meal placement, single serving, type of dish or utensils and inclusion of possible garnish.

Variety in a recipe series will be pointed out. The home economist supports her choices, yet remains open-minded about negative comments. Discussions on format and photography may take place.

The client's suggestions are incorporated and required recipe retesting is conducted.

part III

Recipe Style Guide

1. RECIPE FORMAT

When preparing to write recipe copy, the first question which arises is "what form should the recipe take?" or "how is it best offered to the consumer or end user?" The most important consideration is to provide a recipe which is clear, easy to follow, concise and attractively presented.

Various styles for writing recipes have appeared. While there are many variations on format – dictated by individual project requirements and preference – there are basically three common formats: standard, narrative and action.

The decision as to which style is the best choice is influenced by factors including: the complexity of the recipe, the end use (promotional, cookbook, etc.), limitations on copy space, project criteria and visual preference.

The following information will deal with the main recipe formats, as well as some of the numerous adaptations which appear for consumer use.

With the need to develop recipe copy comes the corresponding need to standardize recipe format both for ease of consumer interpretation and consistency in presentation. A recent review of Canadian consumer publications showed at least six ways of listing measures. Therefore, a "Standard Dual Recipe Format" is also discussed.

Standard Format

The standard format is most commonly used both in cookbooks and promotional material. Within this format, ingredients are listed first, distinctly separate from the method. Metric and/or imperial measures appear on the left and/or right hand side. The method then follows in paragraphs or steps with the recipe yield clearly stated. The following recipe illustrates the standard format.

Very Berry Sauce ◄——**TITLE**   Makes 650 mL
↑
YIELD STATEMENT

Spoon this delicious sauce over vanilla ice cream, puddings or sliced pound cake.
↑
BRIEF INTRODUCTION OR
LEADER LINE – OPTIONAL

MEASURE (METRIC)	INGREDIENT LIST
1	pkg. (425 g/15 oz.) frozen raspberries
500 mL	cranberries
175 mL	granulated sugar
25 mL	cornstarch
25 mL	cold water

METHOD (DIRECTIONS OR PROCEDURES)

In medium saucepan, mix together raspberries, cranberries and sugar. Bring to boil, gently breaking up frozen berries. Blend cornstarch . . .

Common Adaptations of Standard Format

There are many variations of the standard format; however, all are based on the style that ingredients are first, method second.

1. The title and yield may appear in a wide variety of positions – top, bottom, centred or to either side.
2. Measures are seen placed left or right of ingredients with metric and imperial units in either position, or the second in brackets.

VARIATIONS:	500 mL		cranberries	
	2 cups		cranberries	
	500 mL		cranberries	2 cups
	2 cups		cranberries	500 mL
	500 mL	(2 cups)	cranberries	
	2 cups	(500 mL)	cranberries	
	500 mL	2 cups	cranberries	
	2 cups	500 mL	cranberries	

3. When two measures are presented, either imperial or metric may be blocked for special emphasis or clarity and may also have either separate colour or type treatment.

1	pkg. (425 g/15 oz.) frozen raspberries	1
500 mL	cranberries	2 cups
175 mL	granulated sugar	¾ cup
25 mL	cold water	2 tbsp.

4. Occasionally measures and ingredients are written in paragraph style. Such a pattern; however, lacks clarity and should be considered only when space is limited.

Very Berry Sauce

1 pkg. (425 g/15 oz.) frozen raspberries, 500 mL cranberries, 175 mL granulated sugar, 25 mL cold water.
In medium saucepan...

---

5. Much variation is possible in method presentation – allowing for uniqueness and emphasis within recipe copy. Copy may be written in paragraph form, or in steps line by line, marked graphically (.,✔,*) or numbered. The "action" word or key step may be emphasized by listing it first or in bold type. The client's product name may be contrastingly typed or coloured.
6. Recipes requiring two parts (a pie crust and filling) or three parts (cake, cake filling, icing) usually appear in the standard format. The ingredients required for each recipe part may be grouped together and identified with a heading. The method may also be broken down by section under the appropriate heading. The following example illustrates this presentation.

```
┌──────────────────────────────────────────────────────────────────────┐
│                         Cranberry Cobbler                              │
│              Biscuit Base ◄──────── HEADING                            │
│                   125 mL      orange juice                             │
│                   250 mL      brown sugar                              │
│                     1 mL      cinnamon                                 │
│                    25 mL      cornstarch                               │
│                   500 mL      cranberries                              │
│                   500 mL      sliced rhubarb                           │
│                                                                        │
│              Biscuit Topping ◄────────── HEADING                       │
│                   250 mL      all-purpose flour                        │
│                    15 mL      granulated sugar                         │
│                     7 mL      baking powder                            │
│                     2 mL      salt                                     │
│                    50 mL      shortening                               │
│                   125 mL      milk                                     │
│                                                                        │
│   Biscuit base: In medium saucepan, mix together orange juice,        │
│   brown sugar, ◄── BASE METHOD                                         │
│                                                                        │
│   Biscuit Topping: In medium bowl, combine flour, sugar, ◄──── TOPPING │
│   METHOD                                                               │
└──────────────────────────────────────────────────────────────────────┘
```

7. It may be desirable to include comments that are not essential to the recipe, in the recipe copy. Such information could include:
   - preparation time
   - freezing instructions
   - microwave setting
   - suggested usage (snack, main meal)
   - calorie or nutritional content
   - total menu suggestions
   - instructions for high altitude usage
   - garnish ideas

This additional material can appear before or after ingredients or method; placed centre, left or right or included directly in the method.

Narrative Format

The second format is often referred to as the narrative format. This pattern is best used when there are limitations on space or if the recipes are short and uncomplicated. The narrative format, includes ingredients' measures in the method. It may be expanded for detail or condensed for casual recipe ideas and varied like the standard format. However, unless the recipe is particularly short and simple, this format can be difficult to present coherently.

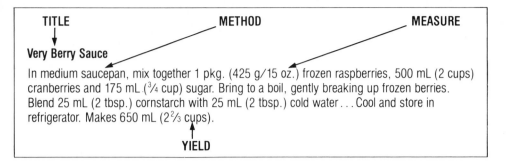

TITLE   **METHOD**   **MEASURE**

Very Berry Sauce

In medium saucepan, mix together 1 pkg. (425 g/15 oz.) frozen raspberries, 500 mL (2 cups) cranberries and 175 mL ($^3/_4$ cup) sugar. Bring to a boil, gently breaking up frozen berries. Blend 25 mL (2 tbsp.) cornstarch with 25 mL (2 tbsp.) cold water... Cool and store in refrigerator. Makes 650 mL (2$^2/_3$ cups).

YIELD

Action Format

This recipe style incorporates elements of the narrative format with the standard format. An attempt is made to clearly list the ingredients required for each particular method step within the method statements. Although this style is easy to follow, it may take more space and can be difficult to arrange economically or attractively on paper – especially when using dual measures.

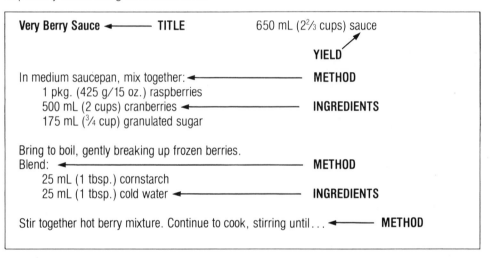

Very Berry Sauce ◄──── TITLE   650 mL (2$^2/_3$ cups) sauce

YIELD

In medium saucepan, mix together: ◄──────── **METHOD**
     1 pkg. (425 g/15 oz.) raspberries
     500 mL (2 cups) cranberries ◄──────── **INGREDIENTS**
     175 mL ($^3/_4$ cup) granulated sugar

Bring to boil, gently breaking up frozen berries.
Blend: ◄──────── **METHOD**
     25 mL (1 tbsp.) cornstarch
     25 mL (1 tbsp.) cold water ◄──────── **INGREDIENTS**

Stir together hot berry mixture. Continue to cook, stirring until... ◄──────── **METHOD**

Variations in this format include placement or choice of metric and/or imperial measures, as well as emphasis on significant method statements and placement of additional information.

Standard Dual Recipe Format

Whenever the recipe development goals allow, the staff home economists at Cardinal Kitchens choose the format which they have named STANDARD DUAL RECIPE FORMAT. Used also by other Canadian food professionals, it presents three clearly separate columns with metric measures first. Recognizing that many consumers are still more comfortable with imperial measures, they are presented second, next to the ingredient name. In the future, with fuller consumer familiarity and acceptance of metric usage, the imperial column can simply be removed with very little format redesign needed.

```
                                    TITLE                              YIELD
                MEASURE                        INGREDIENT
          METRIC           IMPERIAL
          _____        _____           _____
          _____        _____           _____
          _____        _____           _____

   METHOD
          _____
          _____
          _____
```

Long term benefits in promoting uniformity in recipe style are very significant for consumers, the home economics profession and food advertising or marketing personnel.

2. PHOTOGRAPHY, GRAPHICS AND LANGUAGE FOR PROMOTIONAL RECIPES

Graphics or photography in recipe format design is an important element, particularly for recipes developed for product promotion. If printing space allows, creative design will transform a recipe to one which immediately draws the reader's attention. Eye appeal is especially important for recipes appearing in newspapers and magazines or on recipe cards and point-of-purchase material. By using photography and/or graphic design to their fullest potential, a recipe can project a desired mood or atmosphere. Enthusiasm is created for the recipe, as well as for the product. To achieve the intended effect, an endless range of designs are possible.

A home economist in business may work in co-ordination with a graphic designer at this stage of a recipe development project, to determine exactly how various elements will be used.

Not only will graphics make a recipe more visually attractive, they may also assist a particular consumer group. For example, through the use of large wide-spaced print and illustrations of step-by-step preparation methods, recipes for children are made simpler and easy to follow.

Language also plays an important role in graphics and layout selection. For national distribution or promotion, both French and English printing is desirable. (The demand for French material is typically one-fifth to one-quarter that of English but may vary for a particular product.) Since written French usually requires more copy space than written English, approximate layout of dual language recipes requires special planning.

The availability of printing space is a prime factor in determining the recipe format and the language(s) used. Although there could be a necessity of condensing or paraphrasing, (especially the method) clarity, as always, is of utmost importance.

The client's preferences and marketing guidelines will ultimately be the dominant factor when choosing photography and graphic design. However, the client's final decision may be made easier, if supported by a home economist who understands the substantial benefits of imaginative design.

3. RECIPE COPY PRESENTATION
i. Consumer

The following variations of extended recipe copy give creative examples of diagrams, photgraphs of illustrations to further promote a product and its companion recipes. These diagrams suggest various placements of component parts of a visual recipe presentation.

a. The use of step-by-step diagrams to illustrate method can help many consumers, especially less experienced cooks. Additional information can include recipe origin, uses, oven time and temperature, nutrient value, calorie content or serving size.

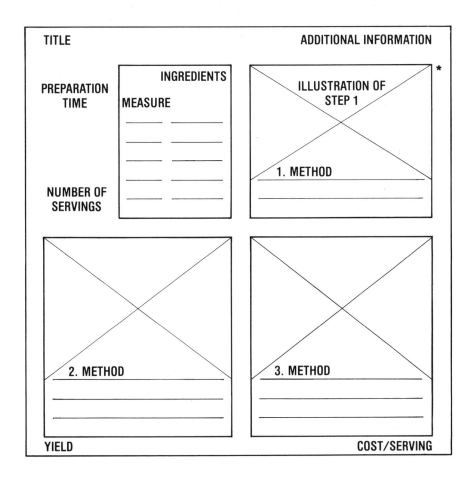

*⊠ means photograph, diagram or illustration.

b. Photographs may show preparation techniques, method, the prepared recipe or the client's product. Most consumers appreciate visual explanations. Dual measures may increase consumer attraction to a recipe and its featured product. Ideas for the recipe's use are practical.

TITLE	MEASURE	YIELD
DESCRIPTION OF **RECIPE'S USE** **AND APPEAL**	**METRIC IMPERIAL INGREDIENTS**	

PROMOTIONAL MATERIAL

METHOD

PHOTOGRAPH OF PREPARED RECIPE

PHOTOGRAPH OF FOOD PRODUCTS MARKETED FORM

c. An outline of required equipment and preparation/cooking time, gives consumers an opportunity to organize prior to recipe preparation. This information also helps children or less experienced cooks. The inclusion of suggested toppings or garnishes may also be appreciated by the consumer.

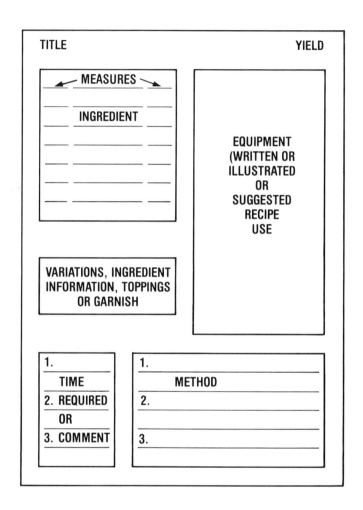

d. Recipes printed on cards offer twice the copy space and are easily available for use or reference. A recipe with an accompanying menu, provides the opportunity to present a festive, gourmet or special-occasion recipe as well as an appropriate meal plan. Cooks like to know what dishes compliment a featured recipe. Companion shopping lists can save time. A work plan and cost per serving also increase efficiency.

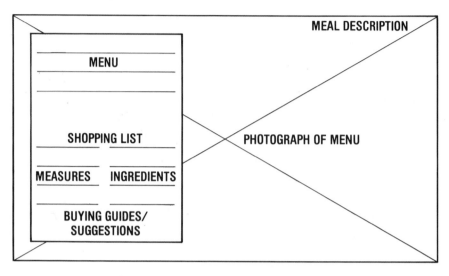

REVERSE SIDE

e. Consumers sometimes need quantity recipes for a whole menu and organizational information for such situations as entertaining or preparing food for their freezers. Planning for preparation is described as are serving suggestions and garnishes. Two or more recipes can be offered, one for main course, one for a dessert.

MENU

| Recipe #1 - Main Course | | Recipe #2 - Dessert |

WORK PLAN

No. 1 RECIPE TITLE (YIELD e.g. 12-14 servings)

DAY BEFORE

1. _____
2. _____

MEASURE	INGREDIENT	MEASURE	INGREDIENT

EARLY IN DAY

1. _____
2. _____

METHOD

SERVING SUGGESTION   **GARNISH**

ONE HOUR BEFORE

1. _____
2. _____
3. _____
4. _____

No. 2 RECIPE TITLE (YIELD)

MEASURE	INGREDIENT	MEASURE	INGREDIENT

JUST BEFORE

1. _____
2. _____

METHOD

ii. Quantity Food Service

Many recipes developed are primarily for quantity food service preparation. The most familiar quantity recipe format used is based on the standard format. It is clear and consistent, either for a recipe card or computer file. Measures are frequently in metric only but weight and volume units are given. If measure or as purchased/edible portion equivalents are available, they are stated. Total yield, if it can be accurately calculated, is valuable in indicating essential quantity cookware or bakeware.

Beverages ◄── CATEGORY TITLE FOR CARD OR COMPUTER FILE   990261 ◄── RECIPE CODE NUMBER

YIELD
(OR NUMBER OF SERVINGS AND PORTION SIZE)   Gazpacho Cocktail ◄── TITLE   Nov-1980 ◄── DATE TESTED

50 servings (150 mL each)

MEASURE (METRIC)

INGREDIENT	WEIGHT	VOLUME	METHOD
Tomato juice		6 cans (1.36 L each)	Combine. Refrigerate 4 h. Strain.
Cucumber, grated	1.5 kg	2 L	
Onion, grated	250 g A.P. 225 g E.P.	250 mL	
Vinegar		50 mL	
Worcestershire sauce		25 mL	
Salt		15 mL	
Sugar		10 mL	

Cucumber slices ◄── GARNISH ──► 50   Garnish each glass with cucumber slice.
INGREDIENT   NUMBER   METHOD

The incorporation of innovative presentation ideas is possible for quantity recipes. Home economists promoting consumer recipes also often consider some of the following options.

Potential Additional Recipe Information

- **Product Promotion:** alternate title • recipe description • recipe meal-time use • promotional information for food product or recipe using food product • company address for requesting additional information or recipes •

- **Photography, Illustrations and/or Diagrams:** one or more samples of raw food or food product • one portion, with or without garnish • recipe quantity in bakeware used • alternate recipe use • alternate bakeware • combinations of recipe variations • recipe variations and related methods, e.g. alternate filling suggestions • appetizers and accompaniments • soups, with garnishes or additions • sandwiches – serving suggestions, accompaniments • entrées, with sauces, garnishes •

- **Alternate Ingredient:** form • measures or combinations of measures, e.g. weight, volume, metric, imperial, unit, as purchased, edible portion • measure for one serving •

- **Alternate Method:** buying • preparation • cooking – individual servings (e.g. microwave, convection, oven, top-of-the-stove), related time, temperature or power • method statements – standard, action or narrative •

- **Alternate Yield:** number of portions – 10, 12, 25(24), 50(48), 100(98) and appropriate ingredient measures, methods and/or cookware requirements • variations of serving size •

- **Other Options:** list of equipment needed or alternates/substitutes • cost/recipe • cost/serving • column for cost of each ingredient • nutrient analysis/serving • calories/serving • required food or food product handling information • storage information (e.g. refrigeration, freezing) • techniques for reconstitution or thawing • suggested garnishes • translations – French, Braille, other languages • blank space for comments or additions •

B Principles Of Recipe Writing

To successfully write a recipe, many guidelines come into effect. Such directions indicate the need for standardization of recipe copy, including description and listing of ingredients and description and presentation of method statements. The following three sections deal systematically with these areas.

1. GENERAL RECIPE WRITING GUIDELINES

a. The appropriate time is necessary when writing and editing a recipe – the process cannot be rushed! If care and concentration are ignored, costly errors may result. The consumer who follows an incorrect recipe not only wastes her time and money, but may also decide all recipes developed for that particular product are worthless. No client can afford to have this happen!

b. At this point, since the recipe has been approved, **NO CHANGES** should be made to the essence of the recipe method and ingredients.

c. Aim for simplicity and conciseness in phrasing, without sacrificing clarity. There is no need to use words or terms which the reader may have to check in a dictionary. Long phrases and large words do nothing except confuse the reader and waste space.

d. Since consumers may appreciate recipes which relay certain aspects of food science technology, an effort is made to incorporate key material into the recipe. For example, a recipe which involves melting chocolate may caution the consumer not to place the ingredient over **HIGH** heat or the chocolate will scorch.

With recipes for microwave cookery, the professional has an added challenge of translating technology into practical simplified "how to" terms.

e. The target market is always kept in mind. For example, recipes for children require added clarity and simplicity. Appropriate vocabulary, meal situation suggestions and format are all equally meaningful.

f. All generic terms and package sizes (both imperial and metric) are checked before writing to ensure they are correct.

g. All ingredients must be listed correctly. (See Part III – Ingredient Listing Statements.)

h. For both the ingredient listing and method statement, standard abbreviations or symbols only are used. (See Part VI – Standard Abbreviations/Symbols.)

i. Accurate terms are essential in describing a method. Care is taken to choose exact terms (e.g. mix, combine or blend). (See Part III – Method Statement Guidelines and Part V – Glossary of Food and Cooking Terms.) The terms, as well as the description of the method, should make sense to the reader.

j. All ingredients listed are included in the method. A count and recount to check is good practice.

k. For metric units, proper SI symbols are chosen for all measurements. (See Part IV – Metric Recipe Development and Style Guide.)

l. Be conscious of terminology in relation to the target market users of the recipe. Two examples follow:

Familiar Canadian terms, such as "wieners", may be more readily accepted by Canadian users than the American, "frankfurters".

Classical ingredient references, such as "scallions", may be a preferable choice over "green onions" for a gourmet recipe series, but could provide an intimidating element for the back panel recipe for a convenience product.

m. After the recipe has been written, the recipe test sheet is attached to the written copy. This allows quick access to original information. At this point, the recipe should be ready for typing or computer entry.

2. INGREDIENT LISTING GUIDELINES

Ingredient listing refers to the actual ingredient, its description as well as the corresponding amount, measure or unit. Because the metric system has adopted the term "measure" (for amounts), this section refers to "measure", whether indicating metric or imperial. Depending on recipe format, the measure may appear beside the description of the ingredient and/or incorporated into the ingredient's description, e.g.

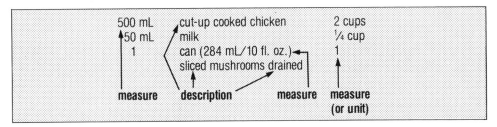

For clarity, ingredient listing guidelines have been categorized in three sections:
- general guidelines;
- ingredient measure guidelines; and
- ingredient description guidelines.

General Guidelines

i. Whether referring to measure or the description of an ingredient, always recheck the information against the test sheet.

ii. Ingredients are listed in order of use, whenever possible. As long as the client's product is a significant ingredient in the recipe, it can be listed first or last to give it more prominence. (See Part V – Key Points from "Guide for Food Manufacturers and Advertisers".)

iii. Most ingredients are listed by generic or common name (in order of use). This pattern is the directive expressed by Consumer and Corporate Affairs Canada. If appropriate as a marketing technique, the client's product (and any other tie-in product) are listed by full brand name and general description.

Ingredient Measure Guidelines

a. Choose **standard abbreviations/symbols** only. (See Part VI – Standard Abbreviations/Symbols.)

b. When referring to **metric units**, use the proper SI symbols. (See Part IV – Metric Recipe Development and Style Guide.)

c. When **listing metric measures** line up the first letter of the measures, e.g.

> 1 L   water
> 125 mL vinegar
> 0.5 mL basil
> 500 g   ground beef

d. Give ingredients in the **easiest unit** of measure without sacrificing clarity, e.g.

> 50 mL (¼ cup) milk
> NOT
> 50 mL (4 tbsp.) milk

e. If it helps the consumer's usual method of purchase, use **weights instead of measures**, particularly when referring to uncooked meat, poultry, fish or cheese, e.g.

> 500 g (1 lb.) ground beef
> RATHER THAN
> 500 mL (2 cups) ground beef

f. When **using whole units** of ingredients, state size most readily available to consumers, e.g.

> 1 pkg. (5.25 oz.) chocolate pie filling mix

When adapting to metric state:

> 1 pkg. (149 g/5.25 oz.) chocolate pie filling mix

As Metric Package Content Sizing – Canada regulations become fully effective, all food packages will be in metric units only.

g. Include weight or fluid measure for **canned products**, not simply unit reference, e.g.

> 1 can (284 mL/10 fl. oz.) tomato soup
> NOT
> 1 can tomato soup

h. List all measures of **packaged ingredients** (except cheese and meats over 1 kg/½ lb.) in ounces, not pounds, e.g.

> 1 can (540 mL/19 fl. oz.) whole kernel corn
> NOT
> 1 can (540 mL/1 lb. 3 oz.) whole kernel corn

i. Itemize all amounts of **cheese** and **diced or cubed meats** in common measure. Give appropriate weights in brackets. If under 1 kg list in grams and if under 1 lb. list in ounces, e.g.

> 250 mL (1 cup) Swiss cheese, shredded (about 113 g/4 oz.)
> 500 mL (2 cups) diced cooked ham (about 500 g/1 lb.)

j. List **approximate quantity of meat** in kilograms whenever meat is listed in units, e.g.

> 8 butterfly pork chops, 5 cm (2 in.) thick (about 0.8 kg).

k. Present **multiple units** of packaged ingredients as follows:

> 2 cans (228 mL/8 fl. oz., each) tomato sauce

l. Avoid using **partial packages** of ingredients where storage or additional use of that ingredient could be inconvenient, e.g.

> 25 mL (2 tbsp.) tomato paste

If there are leftovers, place an asterisk at the conclusion of the recipe and offer suggestions for alternate use, if possible.

m. When preparing a potentially **unfamiliar fruit or vegetable**, or if the fruit or vegetable is cooked, sliced, chopped, or mashed, it is helpful if required amounts or size of that food appear in brackets, e.g.

>250 mL (1 cup) mashed avocado (about 2 medium)
>750 mL (3 cups) thinly sliced cooked potatoes
>(about 3 medium)

n. If an ingredient **amount is not given**, capitalize the first letter of the first word of the ingredient, e.g.

>Yellow food colouring

If amount of ingredient is **written out** in full, capitalize the first letter of the first word, e.g.

>Dash pepper

Ingredient Description Guidelines

a. List the **form or state** of the ingredient very SPECIFICALLY, e.g.

>1 pkg. (250 g) cream cheese, softened, cut into chunks
>5 unpeeled cucumber slices
>1 medium avocado, peeled, pitted and cut into 7 cm (3-in.) pieces

b. Specify **exact types of product** needed, e.g.

>250 mL cake flour
>5 mL ground oregano
>250 mL white grape juice

c. Keep constantly aware of required **food science technology** or **cooking techniques** when describing ingredients and related method, e.g.

>list COLD water when used for blending with flour or cornstarch

d. Using **geographical adjectives** and illustrations indicates that foods are products of the place named, except in cases where the geographical term has losts its significance. (Consumer and Corporate Affairs Canada), e.g.

>1 Spanish onion, diced
>1 mL (¹/₄ tsp.) Worcestershire sauce

Where the goods are not products of the place named and where such description may be considered deceptive or misleading, the product should be described in such a way so as to remove any possible deception.

e. If possible, list **preparation of ingredients** within the ingredient listing, e.g.

>1 apple, diced

Listing preparation prior to stating the method, allows more efficient use of the consumer's time, decreases the chance of recipe failure and saves copy space in the method.

f. If ingredient **amounts** are **used** in the **"as purchased"** form then prepared, list by giving quantity and ingredient, then preparation; separate ingredient and preparation with a comma, e.g.

>2 bananas, mashed
>500 g (1 lb.) chicken, cooked and diced

g. If **ingredients** are **prepared, then** accurately **measured;** the descriptive terms are written preceding the ingredient, from right to left in the order in which they are performed, e.g.

>250 mL (1 cup) chopped peeled cucumber
>500 mL (2 cups) diced cooked chicken

h. If **ingredients** are accurately **measured,** then prepared; the descriptive terms are written following the ingredient from left to right in the order in which they are performed, e.g.

> 250 mL (1 cup) butter, melted
> 250 mL (1 cup) whipping cream, whipped

NOTE: The yield will be approximately 500 mL (2 cups), whereas, if written as:

> 250 mL (1 cup) whipped cream

the amount added in the recipe will be 250 mL (1 cup), since the cream is whipped before measuring. (Descriptive term preceding the ingredient – point g.)

i. Use appropriate **terms for cutting** ingredients. The terms in order of increasing size are:

> minced
> finely chopped
> chopped (use ''diced'' when uniform size is needed)
> coarsely chopped
> cut into X cm (X-in.) pieces, cubes.

j. When referring to pieces over 3 cm (1 in.) long, refer to as **"cut"**, under 3 cm (1 in.) refer to as **"sliced"**, e.g.

> 3 carrots, diagonally cut into 5 cm (2-in.) pieces
> 1 large carrot, thinly sliced

Indicate size of fruits and vegetables only when size will affect the recipe performance.

k. State **reserved liquid or syrups** as follows:

> 1 can (170 g/6 fl. oz.) minced clams, drained (reserve liquid)

If **juices** or any **liquid** are **heated to boiling,** refer to as:

> 250 mL (1 cup) orange juice, heated to boiling

l. Liquid volume in imperial measure is referred to as fluid ounce, not just ounce, e.g.

> 1 can (284 mL/10 fl. oz.) sliced mushrooms
> NOT
> 1 can (284 mL/10 oz.) sliced mushrooms

m. List **alternate or substitute*** ingredients after considering availability, season, cost, popularity of original ingredient and only if there is a fully satisfactory substitute. The first ingredient choice will be the one printed in the method, e.g.

> butter or margarine
> chicken or tuna

If listing two or more ingredients is too long for the space available, asterisk and list at the end of the recipe. *As indicated by Consumer and Corporate Affairs Canada, an imitation food resembles the food imitated in flavour, texture and appearance while substitute foods do not necessarily physically resemble the product replaced. Terms such as "true", "real" and "genuine" should be applied with care and avoided in advertising. Also, foods or ingredients in foods may be described by these terms only when there is an imitation counterpart to that food.

n. Use the **word variation** when another ingredient(s) can be used for a different version, particularly a different flavour. If variations are created by adding a few ingredients to the original recipe, asterisk ingredient if desired and list variation at the end of the recipe.

o. If a **companion recipe** or **suggested topping or garnish** is included with the main recipe, list the companion recipe's name, distinguish it clearly, marking by such means as an asterisk and present that recipe separately.

p. List **optional ingredients** as follows:

> 2 mL (½ tsp.) almond extract (optional)

q. If the **same ingredient is used more than once,** combine if possible in ingredient listing using one of the two following approaches. Clearly separate in the method, giving appropriate measures, e.g.

> 125 mL (½ cup) flour
>
> Method: add 50 mL (¼ cup) flour...add remaining flour
>
> > OR
>
> 125 mL (½ cup) flour, divided
>
> Method: add 50 mL (¼ cup) flour...add remaining flour
>
> > HOWEVER

If combining measures is inappropriate, list in separate measures, in order used, e.g.

> 125 mL (½ cup) milk
>
> 15 mL (1 tbsp.) milk
>
> Method: add 125 mL (½ cup) milk...add remaining milk

r. In ingredient listing, never combine **like ingredients** which are **treated differently,** such as hot and cold juices or whole and sliced fruit.

s. When referring to the **insides of fruit or vegetables,** refer to as:

> FLESH when the fruit or vegetable is whole.
>
> PULP when the natural state of the fruit or vegetable is changed (e.g. cut, peeled, heated, cooked).

3. METHOD STATEMENT GUIDELINES

The method of a recipe usually includes (depending on format) techniques as well as ingredient statements.

Combine chicken, milk and mushrooms.
Simmer, uncovered, stirring frequently, 5 min. Add a dash of salt.
techniques within method   **ingredient statement**

When writing the recipe's method, try to use short sentences and clear, simple directions which can be easily followed. Be descriptive in your terms, especially when working with mixtures which may be unfamiliar to the consumer. e.g. "Beat egg whites until soft peaks form", "beat until foamy throughout" or "mixture thickens as it cools". Make sure the directions are precise and accurate and will not be misinterpreted by some consumers. e.g. "Chill until syrupy" may be interpreted differently among consumers.

Consistency in key phrases is important, if a series is being developed. Try not to confuse the reader with different terms if one phrase can be repeated. Do not assume the reader will remember certain methods; if instructions are required in each recipe, repeat them.

General Method Guidelines

i. By using abbreviations, there is an opportunity for presenting units in short and sometimes clearer form. Depending on available copy space and compatibility with ingredient listing style, abbreviations may be used. If so, use standard abbreviations only. (See Part VI – Standard Abbreviations/Symbols.)

ii. If referring to metric units, use proper SI symbols. (See Part IV – Metric Recipe Development and Style Guide.)

iii. To ensure the written method is consistent with test results, recheck the method against the original test sheet. Also recheck the order of ingredients listed in the ingredient listing against the order used in the method.

iv. In the method, the client's product is usually stated generically.

Ingredient Statements Within Method

a. Use one **general name for ingredient** unless an adjective is also necessary to identify the product or ingredient or is necessary to distinguish between different forms of the same product. The following exceptions are worth noting:

Ingredient listing: 3 eggs, separated
Method Statement: egg yolks or egg whites
Ingredient Listing: vanilla extract
Method Statement: vanilla (all other extracts, repeat the word extract)

b. Try to **state solid ingredient** first as a one step addition to a blended mixture, e.g.
Add tuna and instant seasoning mix blended with water, wine and parsley.

c. When referring to an **uncooked ingredient** in ingredient listing, repeat "uncooked" in method if ingredient is normally expected to be cooked, e.g.
Combine uncooked rice with tomato soup.

d. If the **same ingredient** is used twice in a single recipe but **prepared differently** each time, describe fully, e.g.
Add chopped cooked carrot…garnish with carrot slices.

e. If the **amount is not crucial** to the success of the recipe, and you are only using part of a mixture at a time, state the amount in fractions without defining the exact measure, e.g.
Add half the sauce…

f. If the **amount of water** needed is **not certain** state as:
Add reserved syrup with enough water to equal 250 mL (1 cup).

g. Amounts of a few ingredients (e.g. salt, paprika) may be referred to as **"salt (etc.) to taste".** This allows for individual preferences. Amounts under 0.5 mL ($\frac{1}{8}$ tsp.) are referred to as "dash".

h. When adding a **flour mixture or starch** to a recipe for thickening, always bring to a boil and state as follows:
Add (sifted) flour blended with water. Bring to boil, then simmer, stirring constantly, until sauce is thickened, about 5 min.

i. If **garnish** is **included** in ingredient listing, state as follows:
Ingredient Listing: 125 mL ($\frac{1}{2}$ cup) sliced olives
Method Statement: garnish with olives

If **garnish** is **optional** (and not included in ingredient listing), state as follows:
Garnish, if desired, with sliced olives.

Techniques Within Method

a. State **"mix"** when stirring two or more **like* ingredients** together to form a mixture which has either **distinguishable** or **indistinguishable ingredients**, e.g.

> Mix raisins, coconut and grapes.
> Mix flour, baking powder and salt.

b. State **"combine"** when stirring two or more **unlike* ingredients** together to form a mixture of uniform consistency in which separate ingredients are distinguishable, e.g.

> Combine milk, oil and vanilla.

c. State **"blend"** when stirring two or more **unlike ingredients** together to form a mixture in which separate **ingredients** are **indistinguishable** (homogeneous), e.g.

> Blend icing sugar with butter.

d. Use **"with"** when mixing, blending or combining two ingredients. Use **"and"** when mixing, blending or combining three or more ingredients.

e. State **"fold"** when **ingredient is gently combined** with a mixture so as not to lose any air which has been incorporated into the ingredient, e.g.

> Fold in beaten egg white.

f. State **"pour"** when working with a **mixture** which **flows** easily into the contours of a pan, e.g.

> Pour batter into pan.

g. State **"turn"** when working with **mixture** which easily **loses volume** if overly manipulated, e.g.

> Turn soufflé mixture into pan.

h. State **"spread"** when working with a heavier, thicker **mixture** which **requires** extra **manipulation** to obtain an even layer in the pan.

i. If mixing, combining or blending **four or more ingredients**, state size of container, e.g.

> In small bowl, combine butter, sugar, cinnamon and vanilla.

j. When **all ingredients** are **used** at the **same time**, state as follows:

> In large bowl, combine (blend or mix) all ingredients.

k. When **all ingredients** are used at the **same time except** the **last** ingredient (e.g. parsley), state:

> In large bowl, combine (mix or blend) all ingredients except parsley.

l. State **cookware or bakeware**, prior to the technique and indicate size, if essential, e.g.

> In small saucepan, melt...
> Turn into 2 L (2-qt.) greased casserole.
> Pour into 1.4 L (11'' x 7'') baking pan.

NOTE: baking pan = metal
baking dish = glass
cookie sheet not baking sheet.

m. When referring to **cooking or baking times**, indicate a range of times (e.g. 20-25 min) or a time and a completion phrase, e.g.

> Bake 50 min or until cake springs back when pressed lightly.
> Bake 25 min or until bubbling. (casseroles)
> Bake 20 min or until heated through. (casseroles)
> Bake 10 min or until fish flakes.
> Bake 40 min or until chicken is done. (meats, poultry)

NOTE: Only state one alternative. DO NOT STATE bake 20-25 min or until tender. State, bake 20 min or until tender.

Baking range should be no longer than five minutes, unless total time is long.

n. Cooking **times less than 1 h** should be written in minutes; over 1 h in full hours plus fractions, e.g.

> Bake 30 min at 200°C (400°F).
> Simmer 1¼-1½ h (not 75-90 min).

o. **Time** always comes **before temperature** unless the result is described, e.g.

> Bake 12-15 min at 200°C (400°F).
> Bake at 200°C (400°F) until tender (about 12 min).

p. Try to give both general and specific **tests or temperatures**. This will allow the consumer/end user a double check on important stages, e.g.

> Cook to 114°C (238°F) or until a small amount of syrup forms
> a soft ball in cold water.

q. If possible, try to **state** the **yield separately** from the method. When stating yield try to give the exact number and size of servings to expect, e.g.

> Makes 4-250 mL (1 cup) servings or approximately 1 L (1 qt.).

If exact yield is not known, state as follows:

> Makes 4-6 servings.
> Makes 10-12 servings. (cakes)
> Makes about 4 dozen cookies. (bars)
> Makes about 8 servings. (loaf, pie)
> Makes about 2 L (2 qt.) soup. (homemade)

r. Suggest timing or description for **chilling**, if important to recipe's success, e.g.

> Chill at least 1 h.
> Chill until set. (dessert dishes – not unmoulded)
> Chill until firm. (mousse, unmoulded dishes, pies)

s. If possible, when **marinating** give utensil used as well as timing, e.g.

> Let mixture stand covered at room temperature overnight in
> glass bowl.
> Refrigerate in covered glass bowl, at least 8 h, turning occasionally.

t. If recipe involves **barbecuing**, refer to as broil or grill (metric). Try to give alternate for cooking time, e.g.

> Broil until tender and browned – about 15 min.
> Grill until the meat browns – about 5 min a side.

u. If **cooling food** after cooking, state where the process should take place, e.g.

> Remove from sheet and cool on racks.
> Cool slightly before removing from sheets.
> Cool in the pan before slicing.

v. If **boiling foods**, it may be necessary to specify degree and/or length of boiling, e.g.

> Bring to boil, reduce heat, simmer X min.
> Bring to boil, reduce heat, simmer until tender.
> Add to boiling salted water.
> Return to a full rolling boil.

w. If **simmering food** for **five minutes and under** and stirring is not required, state as:

>Simmer covered.

However, if stirring is required, state as:

>Simmer, uncovered, stirring constantly, X min.

x. If **simmering food** for **over five minutes**, state time as well as frequency of stirring, e.g.:

>Simmer, stirring occasionally, 30 min.
>Simmer, stirring frequently, 15 min.

In a general manner of evaluating like or unlike ingredients, a rating is made in their original (or before recipe presentation) state. Like and unlike ingredients differ in:

>*1. their state of matter (solid or liquid);*
>*2. their solubility (fat or water soluble); or*
>*3. their particle size.*

C Standards For Recipe Editing

Editing (or proofreading,* as it is commonly called) is essential with each new draft or new typing of a recipe. It is preferable that more than one home economist proofreads each recipe copy, as the more involved the professional becomes with her recipe the more difficult it is to spot mistakes. A good technique is to have one home economist read the copy aloud, while the other person precisely checks the written form.

When rewriting and editing a new copy, compare it carefully with the former version. Editing requires concentration and time. The explanation that "it was a typographical error", draws little sympathy from someone who has had a recipe failure due to your incomplete proofreading.

When editing, the following checklist will assist in thoroughness.

*The terms proofreading and editing should not be confused. Editing, is the actual stage when major revision and editing of copy (e.g. grammatical errors) takes place. Proofreading involves reading the edited copy and correcting mistakes such as typographical errors. The efficient home economist first edits a recipe, types it and then proofreads the subsequent copy.

Checklist for Recipe Copy Editing

___ Does the recipe make good common sense?
___ Is the recipe as short and concise as possible?
___ Are ACTUAL ingredients and methods stated?
___ Are the appropriate ingredient and method statements used?
___ Are there an equal number of ingredients in the method and in the ingredient listing?
___ Are there any omissions in temperatures, times or yield?
___ Are accurate terms used for assembling the recipe? e.g. Blend, mix, combine.
___ Is the client's product name spelled correctly, stated correctly and referred to consistently?
___ Are metric or imperial units accurate, consistent and included at all times?
___ Are all generic terms correct?
___ Are all abbreviations and SI symbols correct?
___ Are the correct package sizes stated?
___ Are there any spelling errors?
___ Are there any grammatical errors? e.g. Turn into pan, not, turn in pan.
___ Is there consistency in punctuation? e.g. Dip chops in flour, then in eggs. Blend flour with milk; add to pan.
___ Is there consistency in all key phrases and terminology, when a recipe series is concerned?

While editing and proofreading, mark any changes clearly in pen, as pencil is often difficult to read and will easily smudge. If artboards contain an error never mark the corrections on the board. Outline the corrections on the piece of paper which protects the board. If a printed sample draft is available, correct that.

The following copyreading marks and symbols are widely used in the printing industry.

Correction Desired	Symbol

Spell out a word . . . . ④

Change capital to small letter . . . . ℟

Change small letter to capital . . . . ⌡

To put space between words . . . . 125|mL

To remove the space . . . . meat⌢loaf

To delete a letter and close up . . . . meat⌢sloaf

To delete several letters or words . . . . add the egg

To delete several letters and close up . . . . meat⌢hloaf

To delete one letter and substitute another . . . . bl**e**and

To insert words or several letters . . . . eggs**and**cheese

To transpose letters or words, if adjacent . . . . meatloaf

To insert punctuation:

comma **,**	period **✗**
question **?**	semicolon **;**
colon **:**	hyphen **=**
dash **–**	parenthesis **( )**
apostrophe **'**	

To start a new paragraph . . . . ⁊ or ⌐Combine eggs

To centre material . . . . ⌋Easy Meatloaf⌊

To delete large amounts of copy, draw an X over
the area and box it in . . . . ⊠

To set in boldface type . . . . Brand name

To set in italic type . . . . Brand name

After all corrections have been completed, retype the recipe. Repeat the whole editing and proofreading process until no further errors are detected.

At this point, the final copy can be typed or entered onto a computer. Thoroughly document the latest revision – both for the client and for your own file records.

General Review

As a review of ingredient listing and method statement guidelines and general principles of recipe writing and editing, practise using copyreading marks **to correct the following recipe.** Some examples are based on Part IV – Metric Recipe Development and Style Guide.)

Incorrect Version   POTATOE CASSEROLE

	3	medium potatoes, cooked in skins
75ml	⅓ cup	butter
50ml	4 tbsp.	onion finely chopped
1	1	can (284 mL/10 oz.)
		sliced mushrooms, drained
500 ml	2 cup	cottage cheese, beaten smooth
50ml	¼ cup	sour cream
2	2	eggs, beaten slightly
25ml	2 Tbsp.	flour
1ml	¼ tsp.	rosemary
5ml	1 tsp.	salt
3	3	slices bacon, crumbled
		dash of pepper

Preheat oven to 190°C. Peel potatoes and slice thin. Melt butter in frypan. Add potatoes and onion; cook over moderate heat, turning occassionally with spatula, until lighlty browned. Mix together cottage cheese, sour cream, eggs, fluor, rosemary, salt and pepper. Gently fold in potatoes Pour in 1.5 l (1½ Quart) rectangular casserole. Bake 30 to 35 minutes or until set. Prior to serving top with crumbled bacon.

To assess how thorough you were, check the corrected version that follows.

Corrected Version   POTATO CASSEROLE   *Makes 4 to 6 Servings*

3	3	medium potatoes, cooked in skins
75ml	⅓ cup	butter
¼ cup ~~50ml~~	~~4 tbsp.~~	onion, finely chopped
1	1	can (284 mL/10 oz.) *fl.*
		sliced mushrooms, drained
500 ml	2 cups	cottage cheese, beaten smooth
50ml	¼ cup	sour cream
2	2	eggs, beaten slightly
25ml	2 Tbsp.	flour
1ml	¼ tsp.	rosemary
and mushrooms 5ml	1 tsp.	salt *cooked*
3	3	slices, bacon, crumbled
		dash of pepper

Blend   *Turn (375°F)*

Preheat oven to 190°C. Peel potatoes and slice thin. Melt butter in frypan. Add potatoes ~~and~~ onion; cook over moderate heat, turning occassionally with spatula, until lightly browned. ~~Mix together~~ cottage cheese, sour cream, eggs, flour, rosemary, salt and pepper. ~~Gently~~ fold in potatoes ~~Pour in~~ 1.5 L (1½ ~~Quart~~) rectangular casserole. Bake 30 ~~to 35 minutes~~ or until set. ~~Prior to serving~~ top with crumbled bacon. *at.*

D Summary

Recipe Format and Visual Presentation

1. Recipe Format
There are basically three common formats – standard, narrative and action – and all have numerous variations, advantages or disadvantages.

To promote standardized recipe format a "Standard Dual Recipe Format" is discussed.

2. Photography, Graphics and Language for Promotional Recipes
By choosing from an endless range of designs, recipe copy can have eye appeal, project a desired mood or atmosphere and create positive attitudes for a product.

Design and layout will need special consideration when working with translated recipes.

3. Recipe Copy Presentation
Diagrams, photographs or illustrations can be utilized to further promote a product and its companion recipes.

Although the majority of quantity recipes use the standard format, many innovative presentation ideas are possible.

General Principles of Recipe Writing

The home economist will follow general guidelines when writing a recipe. She will also incorporate guidelines relating to:

1. ingredient listing; and
2. method statements.

Standards for Recipe Editing

By using a checklist, the home economist edits copy to perfect the written recipe. The use of copyreading marks may prove helpful to communicate clearly with the printers.

part IV

Metric Recipe Development and Style Guide

A Introduction

The framework for the adoption of the SI metric system in Canada is now in place. Since Canada's definite commitment to SI metric in 1971, much progress has been made. The Metric Commission Canada, established as an ad hoc commission in 1971, has organized extensive voluntary input from Canadian industry and other representatives. The Style Guide for Metric Recipes prepared by one of these committees on which the Canadian Home Economics Association (CHEA) participated, is the generally accepted basis for the development of metric recipes in Canada. The aims have been:

1. conversion in a manner that will produce the greatest net benefit to the Canadian economy;
2. emphasis on thinking visually in metric rather than conversion; and
3. simplification of conversion to encourage acceptance.

Similar guidelines are the basis for metric recipe development in the U.S.A., where metrication – although moving slower than in Canada – is also happening.

Benefits of SI Metric System

As part of an internationally recognized system, cooking measures are now standardized and compatible with measures used in such other areas of consumer interest as horticulture and prescription drugs. The use of rational metric units in products has made comparison shopping easier. Proliferation of product package sizes has generally been reduced when changed to metric. In a broader sense, functioning in metric can create Canadian jobs, since world markets operate largely with or require metric goods.

Similarities with Imperial* System

Many aspects of recipe development remain the same as for imperial recipes, (sometimes called traditional or American recipes). Recipes continue to be prepared in North America, according to techniques based on volume measurements. (Even in Europe, where cooking is based on weight measurement, a certain trend toward volume measures is developing.)

The same cookware, bakeware and appliances are suitable for metric, and the same overall standardization and sensory appeal can result.

Recipes from both metric and imperial sources continue to be prepared and enjoyed. New or adapted metric recipes need metric measures. Traditional recipes continue to require imperial measures. The key to successful development of metric recipes is to use standard Canadian metric measures (see details in Section C of this Part).

Whatever the recipe origin, an individual recipe should be prepared with all metric measures or all imperial measures – not with a combination.

Common understanding of the term, referring to measurement system already established in Canada, before introduction of metric system.

B SI Metric Units

Adaptation to the metric system means thinking in terms of millilitres and litres instead of tablespoons, cups, pints, quarts and gallons – Celsius instead of Fahrenheit degrees – grams and kilograms instead of ounces and pounds – and millimetres, centimetres and metres instead of inches, feet and yards.

SI Metric Units/Units Used With Metric

Characteristic	Name of Unit	Symbol
Temperature	degree Celsius	°C
Volume	litre	L
	millilitre	mL
Mass	kilogram	kg
	gram	g
	milligram	mg
Length	metre	m
	centimetre	cm
	millimetre	mm
Energy	joule	J
	kilojoule	kJ
	watt	W
Pressure	kilopascals	kPa
Time	second	s
	minute	min
	hour	h

Common Prefixes For Consumer Use

Prefix	Multiplying Factor	Length	Volume	Mass
kilo	1000	kilometre		kilogram
(unit)		metre	litre	gram
centi	0.01	centimetre		
milli	0.001	millimetre	millilitre	milligram

Rules for Writing Symbols

Metric units are expressed in the universally recognized language of measurements, called SI (International System of Units).

One of the main advantages of SI involves the use for each unit, of a unique symbol, which is not an abbreviation. These symbols, as compared to traditional abbreviations, are charted in Part VI.

When writing metric values within the recipe copy, the following rules should be applied.

1. The symbols are always printed in Roman upright type.*
2. The symbols do not change in the plural, e.g. 10 km (not 10 kms).
3. Symbols are never written with a period at the end except when the symbols occur at the end of a sentence.
4. When using a decimal, always place a zero before the decimal point, e.g. 0.45 kg (not .45 kg).
5. Spaces are used instead of commas to divide a long number, e.g. 21 000.
6. There is a space between the number and the symbol, e.g. 90 g,
   but when the first character of a symbol is not a letter, no space is left, e.g. 45°C.
7. Temperatures are either written as degree Celsius or as °C, not degree °C.
8. Litre is written "re" not "er", as is metre.
9. Symbols are written in lower case, except the symbol for litre or where the unit is derived from a proper name,

   e.g. kg but J (Joule)   °C (Celsius)   L (Litre)
              Pa (Pascal)   W (Watt)

10. When numbers are used with symbols, numbers are not written out, e.g. 5 L, not five L.

*See RECIPES in this handbook; type in charts and tables varies.

The following example illustrates metric symbols and format in a recipe. Ingredients are given in quantities convenient to measure, using standard Canadian metric measures. Note how the numbers are aligned for easier reading.

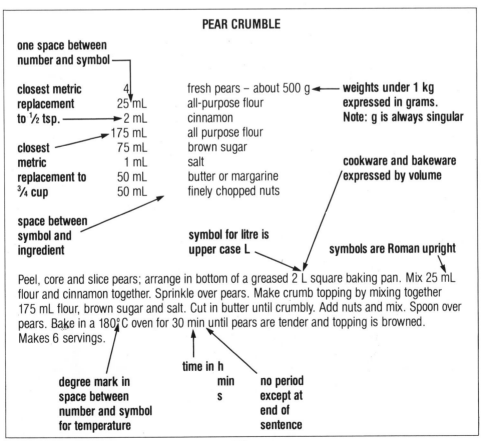

PEAR CRUMBLE

one space between
number and symbol

closest metric   4   fresh pears – about 500 g ⟵ weights under 1 kg
replacement   25 mL   all-purpose flour   expressed in grams.
to ½ tsp. ⟶ 2 mL   cinnamon   Note: g is always singular
           ⟶ 175 mL   all purpose flour
closest   75 mL   brown sugar
metric   1 mL   salt   cookware and bakeware
replacement to   50 mL   butter or margarine   expressed by volume
¾ cup   50 mL   finely chopped nuts

space between
symbol and   symbol for litre is
ingredient   upper case L   symbols are Roman upright

Peel, core and slice pears; arrange in bottom of a greased 2 L square baking pan. Mix 25 mL flour and cinnamon together. Sprinkle over pears. Make crumb topping by mixing together 175 mL flour, brown sugar and salt. Cut in butter until crumbly. Add nuts and mix. Spoon over pears. Bake in a 180°C oven for 30 min until pears are tender and topping is browned. Makes 6 servings.

                    time in h
degree mark in   min   no period
space between   s   except at
number and symbol   end of
for temperature   sentence

C Metric Cooking Measures

The food professional preparing metric recipes will need as basic equipment a set of standard Canadian metric measures (described under Canadian General Standards Board National Standard CAN 2-263-M.77).

The standard set for household use (consumer recipes) includes:

1. liquid measures;
2. dry measures; and
3. small liquid and dry measures.

Standard Household Measures

STANDARD CANADIAN METRIC MEASURES
(always referred to as measures – not cups)

IMPERIAL MEASURES
(shown for general comparison of similarities and differences only – not to be used as equivalents)

Liquid Measures

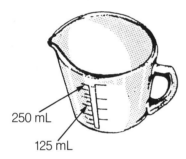

250 mL
125 mL

available in 3 sizes:
250 mL – 25 mL graduations
500 mL – 50 mL graduations
1 L (1 000 mL) – 50 mL graduations

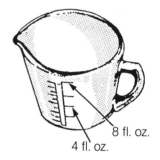

8 fl. oz.
4 fl. oz.

available in assorted sizes:
1 cup
2 cups
4 cups

Dry Measures

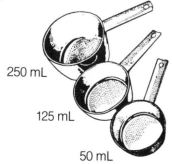

250 mL
125 mL
50 mL

1 cup
½ cup
⅓ cup
¼ cup

Small Liquid and Dry Measures

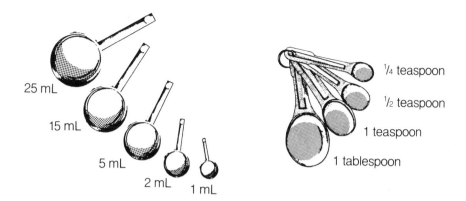

25 mL

15 mL

5 mL

2 mL   1 mL

¼ teaspoon

½ teaspoon

1 teaspoon

1 tablespoon

Note: Avoid the use of small and large dry measures which carry a combination measure notation on individual items, e.g. 113 mL (½ cup).

Metric measures are the same for the U.S.A. as described under American National Standard ANSI Z61.1.

While imperial measures may appear similar to metric ones, they are not inter-changeable. Use metric measures with metric recipes, imperial measures with traditional recipes.

The 250 mL measure replaces the eight ounce cup and involves about a five percent increase in capacity.

Since the 250 mL liquid measure is graduated in 25 mL divisions and both the 500 mL and 1 L measure are graduated in 50 mL divisions, certain cooking ingredients will need to be rounded up or down. Volumes of less than 250 mL should be rounded to nearest 25 mL whereas volumes greater than 250 mL should be rounded to nearest 50 mL.

Volumes greater than 1 000 mL (1 L) are expressed as litres and should be rounded to one decimal place, or if possible, to the nearest whole litre. Anything under 1 L is expressed in millilitres.

Measure ingredients with a minimum of measures – no more than two, if possible, e.g.

i. Measuring 200 mL flour would require the use of four 50 mL measures or one 125 mL, one 50 mL and one 25 mL dry measure. During recipe development, change amount to 175 mL or 250 mL.

ii. Acceptable small quantities would be 1, 2, 3, 4, 5, 6, 7, 10, 15, 20, 25 mL, e.g. Measuring 8 mL baking soda would require the use of 1 mL, 2 mL and 5 mL measure. Change to 7 mL or 10 mL.

The following table may be used to adapt SMALL volume quantities (up to 250 mL/ 1 cup) or for recipes in which proportions are not critical.

Reasonable Replacement Values

0.5 mL replaces ⅛ tsp.	50 mL replaces ¼ cup
1 mL replaces ¼ tsp.	75 mL replaces ⅓ cup
2 mL replaces ½ tsp.	125 mL replaces ½ cup
5 mL replaces 1 tsp.	150 mL replaces ⅔ cup
15 mL replaces 1 tbsp.	175 mL replaces ¾ cup
25 mL replaces 2 tbsp.	250 mL replaces 1 cup
50 mL replaces 3 tbsp.	

However, this replacement system is NOT SUITABLE for large quantities, or in cases of critical proportions. Too much error can be introduced if one ingredient is rounded up or down simply for ease in measuring – without considering the relationships with other recipe ingredients. If this is the case, exact conversions are made first and then rounded to closest convenient measure.

About Canadian And U.S. Measurements – Precise Calculations

There is a widespread awareness of the common differences between Canadian and U.S. measures for such items as gallons (Cdn. – 160 fl. oz.; U.S. – 128 fl. oz.). However, there are certain less known facts regarding Canadian/U.S. measures that may be necessary for the home economist to know. Relating to volume measures of items, this information would not be for presentation to consumers/end users, but would help the food professional contribute knowledgeably to such items as promotional recipe application, as compared to package content declaration. Consider the following:

i. The Canadian and U.S. fluid oz.* are different:
   (for the measure of volume or capacity)
   1 Canadian fluid oz. = 28.4 mL
   1 U.S. fluid oz.   = 29.57 mL
   *not to be confused with oz. when referring to weight; 28.4 g = 1 oz. There is no difference between Canadian and U.S. (weight) oz.

ii. In Canada, household measures for recipes and package directions are based on volume. This volume measure has been used in households for not only liquids such as water and milk, but also for such dry ingredients as flour, sugar and shortening.

iii. In 1954, Canada adopted as its official cup measure for recipes, an 8 U.S. fl. oz. cup.
   1 (8 U.S. fl. oz.) cup = 237 mL (29.57 mL x 8 fl. oz.)

Procedure For Recipe Adaptation

Metric adaptation leads to sensory acceptance of a recipe and arrival at that point is not simply determined by mathematical conversions on paper. Recipes must be physically tested, in all but rare cases. A recipe presented in dual form should be equally acceptable and as similar as possible in both metric and imperial. They cannot always be expected to taste identical, due to small differences in proportion.

Adapting A Recipe From Imperial To Metric

Recipes adapted to the metric form have a clean, streamlined appearance with the psychological message of efficiency and ease of preparation. Notice the uncluttered presentation of the following Chocolate Chip Cookie recipe:

Revised Metric Recipe* – (After Testing)

"CHOCOLATE CHIP COOKIES"

425 mL	all-purpose flour
2 mL	baking soda
2 mL	salt
225 mL	butter or margarine
175 mL	granulated sugar
175 mL	lightly packed brown sugar
1	egg
5 mL	vanilla
1	pkg. (175 g) unsweetened chocolate chips
125 mL	chopped nuts

Preheat oven to 190°C.
Lightly grease a cookie sheet.
Sift together flour, baking soda and salt. Cream butter and sugars together. Beat in egg and vanilla until light and fluffy. Stir in dry ingredients with chocolate chips and nuts. Drop batter from a teaspoon about 5 cm apart on cookie sheet. Bake for 8 min, or until golden brown. Makes 4 to 5 dozen.

This metric recipe was adapted from imperial measures by the following steps:

Step 1

Replace the ingredient listing for a traditional imperial recipe with the initial metric values, e.g.:

"CHOCOLATE CHIP COOKIES"*

Imperial Measures	Ingredients	Initial Metric Values
		STANDARD STEP 1
1¾ cups	all-purpose flour	437.5 mL**
½ tsp.	baking soda	2.5 mL**
½ tsp.	salt	2.5 mL**
1 cup	butter or margarine	250 mL
⅔ cup	granulated sugar	167 mL**
⅔ cup	lightly packed brown sugar	167 mL**
1	egg	1
1 tsp.	vanilla	5 mL
1	package (6 oz.) unsweetened chocolate chips	250 mL
½ cup	chopped nuts	125 mL

Preheat oven to 375°F.

Lightly grease cookie sheet.

Stir together flour, baking soda and salt. Cream butter and sugars together. Beat in egg and vanilla until light and fluffy. Stir in dry ingredients with chocolate chips and nuts. Drop batter from a teaspoon about 2 inches apart on cookie sheet. Bake for 8 min, or until golden brown. Makes 4 to 5 dozen.

Step 2

For easy measuring, the amounts marked with a double-asterisk** required rounding to whole numbers or to multiples of 25. Testing showed sugar amounts could be increased if shortening was decreased.

Step 3

The revised recipe is given above. Note that the metric symbols are aligned and large quantities are in multiples of 25.

Alternate Step 1

An Alternate Step 1 of this method may represent greater efficiency in producing metric and traditional recipes, which are as similar as possible – especially when critical proportions are involved. The basic difference is that calculations for all critical ingredients are based on 1 cup = 237 mL, instead of the rounded 1 cup = 250 mL replacement value. Since test kitchen recipe testing is time-consuming and costly, this method is recommended, but is not suggested for teaching to consumers since simplicity in approach overrides precision in end results.

Recipes are based on examples offered by CHEA Metric Style Guide Committee.

The Transition Period

The challenge for the Canadian food professional is to interpret and simplify the final stages of metric system acceptance in this country. With time, more American recipes will be presented in metric measures. Food service recipes remain primarily metric. The development of metric recipes only, is the ideal, but during the transition period from one system to another, there are many variations. Despite familiarity with convention and guidelines for metric adaptation, actual implementation may be awkward.

Advantages of metric recipes, as well as advantages and disadvantages of offering recipes in both metric and imperial measures are now identified. This handbook helps to guide professionals to the appropriate approach for specific project goals.

Advantages Of Metric Recipes

• As leaders in accepting and implementing change, home economists are ready to offer the Canadian public new metric recipes.
• Metric recipes have a streamlined appearance with the compatible connotation of simplicity.
• Metric units are fewer in number and are in easy-to-use multiples.
• Less confusion exists when one system only is presented and that system corresponds to food and food product labelling and purchasing information.
• Since the metric system is used widely throughout the world, an incentive exists for metric recipes.

Advantages Of Dual System Recipes

• A recipe which incorporates both systems may receive greater acceptance since it will not exclude those people who use only metric or imperial measures.
• When using both measuring systems, recipes may be viewed as current, up-to-date and new.
• A recipe which uses both systems, accommodates both metric and traditional cookware and bakeware.
• From the management/marketing viewpoint, the consumer is offered a choice so she can be "comfortable" with imperial measures or "adventuresome/progressive" with metric. Using both does not eliminate a product sale. The food company can be seen as catering to everyone.
• Both systems can be presented quite neatly, with very little extra copy space.

Disadvantages Of Dual Measures

• Some consumers may feel the dual recipe is too confusing with more room for error by switching from one to another. It may be felt there are too many rows or columns of figures.
• Confusion may also occur if metric measures are compared with imperial. If a recipe is altered when adapting from imperial and in the process, two different metric equivalents are used for one imperial measurement value, the consumer may feel there is a mistake in the recipe.
• The recipe may appear more complicated with additional temperatures and measurements.
• The consumer may be tempted to use a combination of both measures if they do not have a complete set of either. This practice is definitely undesirable.

F Tables For Metric Adaptation

1. Weight Replacement Values

Metric g	Imperial lb.
125	¼
250	½
350	¾
500	1
625	1¼
750	1½
875	1¾
1 000 or 1 kg	2
1 500 or 1.5 kg	3
2 000 or 2 kg	4⅓
2 250 or 2.2 kg	5
4 500 or 4.5 kg	10
5 000 or 5 kg	11

> Replacement values are rounded.
> (See also precise equivalents –
> Part VI, Table B).

When converting to metric, the mass is rounded to nearest 10 g* if under 1 kg. If over 1 kg, round mass to the nearest kilogram whenever possible.

Mass under 1 kg is expressed in grams (g); over 1 kg is expressed in kilograms and rounded to one decimal place, e.g.

545 g fat rounds to 550 g

8 500 g ground beef becomes 8.5 kg

Exception: Quantities of meat under 1 kg. Meat is expressed as a decimal of a kilogram.

2. Linear Dimension Replacement Values

Metric	Imperial in.
3 mm	⅛
6 mm	¼
1 cm	½
2 cm	¾
2.5 cm	1
3 cm	1¼
4 cm	1½
4.5 cm	1¾
5 cm	2

For converting larger measures, always calculate 2.5 cm per inch. For kitchen metrics, length is converted to whole numbers whenever possible e.g. Carrots cut in 1-inch strips – exact conversion would be 2.5, but is rounded to 2 cm or 3 cm strips.

EXCEPTION: In certain cases, the rounded amount will not be accurate enough to ensure good results. For example, stewing beef would be cut in 2.5 cm pieces as 2 cm cubes are too small and 3 cm cubes are too large.

Use 1, 2, 3, 4, 5 cm to denote thickness of meat.

3. Cookware and Bakeware Replacement Values

Existing cookware and bakeware is quite acceptable for metric recipes.

To determine the volume of conventional pans for use in metric recipes, fill the pan with water using a metric liquid measure. Consider it full when the water first makes contact with a straight edged object (e.g. ruler) placed across the top of the container. For example, if an 8-inch square cake pan is filled with water, the volume may measure 1 900 mL. This is approximately 2 000 mL and will be suitable for a recipe calling for a 2 L cake pan.

	Metric			Imperial	
ROUND PANS:	Diameter (cm)	Depth (cm)	Volume (L)	Diameter (in.)	Depth (in.)
Cake	20	4	1.2	8	1½
	22 or 23	3.5	1.5	9	1⅜
Tube	20	10	1.5	8	4
	22 or 23	10 or 11	2.5	9	4
	25	11	3	10	4½
Pie Plates	20	4	750 mL	8	1½
	22 or 23	4	1	9	1½
	25	4.5	1.5	10	1¾
Fruit Cake	15	7.5	1.2	6	3
	22	7.5	2.5	9	3
	30	7.5	4.5	12	3
SQUARE PANS:	Side (cm)	Depth (cm)	Volume (L)	Side (in.)	Depth (in.)
Cake	20	5	2	8	2
	21	5	2	8½	2
	22 or 23	4.3	2	9	1¾

RECTANGULAR PANS:	Length (cm)	Width (cm)	Depth (cm)	Volume (L)	Length (in.)	Width (in.)	Depth (in.)
Cake	28	17	3.7	2	11	7	1½
	30	19	4.5	3	12	8	1¾
	34	22	4	3.5	13	9	1¾
Jelly Roll	40	25	2	1	15	10	¾
	43	35	2	2	17	14	¾
Loaf	21	12	6.5	1.5	8½	4½	2⅝
	23	13	6	2	9	5	2½
	25	15	6.5	3	9¾	5¾	2½
Cookie Sheet	38	30	–	–	15	12	–

	Metric	Imperial
CASSEROLES:	Volume (L)	Volume
	1.5	1½ qt. (U.S.) – 6 cups (Cdn.)
	2	2 qt. (U.S.) – 8 cups (Cdn.)
	1.5	1½ qt. (Cdn.)
	2	2 qt. (Cdn.)
SAUCEPANS AND KETTLES:	Volume (L)	Volume (Cdn. qt.)
	750 mL	26 oz.
	1	32 oz.
	1.5	1½
	2	1¾
	3	2½
	4	3½
	5	4½
MUFFIN TINS:	Volume (mL) (for each cup)	
	25	
	50	
	75	
	larger sizes in multiples of 25 mL	
MIXING BOWLS:	Volume (L)	Volume (cups)
	1	4
	1.5	6
	2	8
	2.5	10
	3	12

ROASTING PANS: Size expressed as its length x width x depth and its level full capacity.
No recommended sizes.

4. Ladles and Scoops Replacement Values

	millilitres	replaces	ounces
Ladles	30		1
	50		2
	125		4
	200		6
	250		8
	350		12
Scoops	30		1
	50		1¾
	60		2
	85		3
	100		3½

5. Temperature Replacement Values

60°C – 140°F	190°C – 375°F
70°C – 150°F	200°C – 400°F
80°C – 170°F	220°C – 425°F
100°C – 200°F	230°C – 450°F
120°C – 250°F	240°C – 475°F
140°C – 275°F	260°C – 500°F
150°C – 300°F	270°C – 525°F
160°C – 325°F	290°C – 550°F
180°C – 350°F	

GRILL (E) replaces broil.

Refrigerator temperature: 4°C replaces 40°F
Freezer temperature: – 18°C replaces 0°F

6. Volume and Weight Equivalents of Canned and Packaged Goods

The range of sizes allowed for all consumer packaged goods is fully outlined in the regulations for Metric Package Content Sizing – Canada defined by the Metric Commission Canada.

Net quantity declaration by metric unit of Canadian FLUID VOLUME (foods packed in jars and most canned goods).

mL	fl. oz.	mL	fl. oz.
114	4	341	12
128	4½	398	14
142	5	455	16
156	5½	540	19
170	6	682	24
175	6½	739	26
199	7	796	28
227	8	1 L	35.2
250	8.8	1.36 L	48
284	10	2.27 L	80
		2.84 L	100

7. Pressure Replacement Values

Pressure for pressure cookers and canners is measured in kilopascals (kPa) instead of pounds per square inch (PSI).

kPa	replaces	PSI
35		5
70		10
100		15

G Summary

Introduction

With the adoption of the SI metric system in Canada, cooking measures are now standardized, comparison shopping is easier and proliferation of product package sizes is less common.

Many aspects of recipe development remain the same as for imperial recipes; volume measure is still implemented and the same cookware, bakeware and appliances are used.

Only metric measures should be used when preparing metric recipes – imperial measures for imperial recipes.

SI Metric Units

Adaptation to the metric system means thinking in terms of new units. Each unit has its own unique symbol which is not an abbreviation.

Specific rules must be applied when writing metric values within recipe copy.

Metric Cooking Measures

The standard set of metric cooking measures includes:
1. liquid measures (available in 250 mL, 500 mL or 1 L size);
2. dry measures (50 mL, 125 mL, 250 mL); and
3. small liquid and dry measures (1 mL, 2 mL, 5 mL, 15 mL, 25 mL).

When measuring ingredients certain cooking items will need rounding; however, ingredients are still measured using a minimum of measures.

Knowledge of the differences between Canadian and U.S. measurements will assist the food professional.

Procedure for Recipe Adaptation

Metric adaptation is not determined by mathematical conversion only. In all but a few cases, the recipe must be physically tested.

Specific steps must be followed for metric adaptation.

The Transition Period

Even though actual implementation of metric only recipes may be resisted, the home economist is challenged to interpret and simplify metric system acceptance.

Professionals who weigh the advantages of metric recipes against the advantages and disadvantages of dual recipes will discover the best approach for specific project goals.

Tables for Metric Adaptation

For easy reference, basic metric replacement values – weight, linear dimensions, cookware and bakeware, ladles and scoops, temperature and volume and weight equivalents of canned and packaged goods – are listed.

part V

Resource Information

This collection of resource information relates to many previously discussed topics. It is an accessible source for material repeatedly referenced by experienced food professionals.

Canada's Food Guide

Eat a variety of foods from each group every day

milk and milk products
Children up to
11 years 2-3 servings
Adolescents 3-4 servings
Pregnant and nursing
women 3-4 servings
Adults 2 servings

meat, fish, poultry and alternates 2 servings

breads and cereals 3-5 servings
whole grain or enriched

fruits and vegetables 4-5 servings
Include at least two vegetables.

Health
and Welfare
Canada
Santé et
Bien-être social
Canada

Canadä

Canada's Food Guide can assist in helping Canadians make wise food selections. Food professionals benefit by its reminder to focus on the whole menu, and also on the type and variety of daily food intake for

Variety

Choose different kinds of foods from within each group in appropriate numbers of servings and portion sizes.

Energy Balance

Needs vary with age, sex and activity. Balance energy intake from foods with energy output from physical activity to control weight. Foods selected according to the Guide can supply 4000 – 6000 kJ (kilojoules) (1000 – 1400 kilocalories). For additional energy, increase the number and size of servings from the various food groups and/or add other foods.

Moderation

Select and prepare foods with limited amounts of fat, sugar and salt. If alcohol is consumed, use limited amounts.

milk and milk products

Children up to 11 years	2-3 servings
Adolescents	3-4 servings
Pregnant and nursing women	3-4 servings
Adults	2 servings

Skim, 2%, whole, buttermilk, reconstituted dry or evaporated milk may be used as a beverage or as the main ingredient in other foods. Cheese may also be chosen.

Some examples of one serving
250 mL (1 cup) milk
175 mL (¾ cup) yoghurt
45 g (1½ ounces) cheddar or process cheese

In addition, a supplement of vitamin D is recommended when milk is consumed which does not contain added vitamin D.

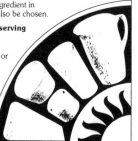

meat, fish, poultry and alternates
2 servings

Some examples of one serving
60 to 90 g (2–3 ounces) cooked lean meat, fish, poultry or liver
60 mL (4 tablespoons) peanut butter
250 mL (1 cup) cooked dried peas, beans or lentils
125 mL (½ cup) nuts or seeds
60 g (2 ounces) cheddar cheese
125 mL (½ cup) cottage cheese
2 eggs

breads and cereals
3-5 servings

whole grain or enriched. Whole grain products are recommended.

Some examples of one serving
1 slice bread
125 mL (½ cup) cooked cereal
175 mL (¾ cup) ready-to-eat cereal
1 roll or muffin
125 to 175 mL (½ – ¾ cup) cooked rice, macaroni, spaghetti or noodles
½ hamburger or wiener bun

fruits and vegetables
4-5 servings

Include at least two vegetables.

Choose a variety of both vegetables and fruits — cooked, raw or their juices. Include yellow, green or green leafy vegetables.

Some examples of one serving
125 mL (½ cup) vegetables or fruits – fresh, frozen or canned
125 mL (½ cup) juice – fresh, frozen or canned
1 medium-sized potato, carrot, tomato, peach, apple, orange or banana

persons of all ages.

Appropriate portion sizes from the four food groups are suggested and help determine yield in recipe development.

Additional Portion Sizes Compatible with Canada's Food Guide

Food Classification	Explanation	Metric Serving Size
BAKED FOODS		
breads	loaves	2 cm thick slice (1/8 of 2 L loaf pan)
cakes	sponges	1/10 of 3 L tube pan
cookies, bars and squares	3 L baking pan	3 cm thick square cut 8 x 3 to yield 24 bars (each serving is 2 bars)
	2 L baking pan	cut 6 x 4 to yield 24 squares (each serving is 2 squares)
	2 L baking pan	3 cm thick cut 4 x 4 to yield 16 squares (each serving is 2 squares)
DAIRY FOODS		
cheese	cheese spread	25 mL (30 g/sandwich)
	flavoured cream cheese	25 mL (25 g/sandwich)
cream	whipped cream	50 mL/serving 625 mL/1 L pie (filling)
ice cream, ice milk	commercial	125 mL
DESSERTS		
pudding	with milk	125 mL
whip-type		150 mL
MAIN DISHES		
casserole	tuna (30 g) or cheese, noodles and sauce	250 mL
meat	beef (60 g), vegetables including potatoes	375 mL
	chunks of meat and sauce	200 mL combined (90 g meat) 250 mL pasta
	meatballs and sauce	90 g cooked meat (3 balls, 3 cm each) 50-60 mL sauce
	meat, cheese and pasta	1/4 of a 1.5 L pan
SALADS		
green		250 mL
jellied, macaroni, potato and coleslaw		125 mL
meat, poultry	meat and rice	200 mL
SALAD DRESSING		15 mL
SAUCES, GRAVIES		25 mL
SOUPS	clear and cream	250 mL

B Key Points from "Guide for Food Manufacturers and Advertisers", Consumer and Corporate Affairs, Canada

In March, 1984 Consumer and Corporate Affairs Canada issued a useful and enlightening Guide for Food Manufacturers and Advertisers. This guide lists many directives which apply directly, or indirectly, to recipe development. Information presented here, cites or paraphrases comments from that guide, which replaces the 1961 version prepared by the Food and Drug Directorate. It is stated that "interpretations and explanations in the new guide have been in place for some time, but now their implementation by directive or memoranda or on an individual basis has been consolidated into a single reference". Some labels and advertisements may not be fully in accordance with the new guidelines and in these instances, manufacturers and advertisers will be given adequate time (6-12 months) to comply.

Regarding legislation, excerpts from the Food and Drugs Act and Consumer Packaging and Labelling Act are the most important in general regulation of food advertising. "Advertisement includes any representation by any means whatever for the purpose of promoting directly or indirectly the sale or disposal of any food, drug, cosmetic or device." (Food and Drugs Act) It continues, "no person shall label, package, treat, process or advertise any food in a manner that is false, misleading or deceptive or is likely to create an erroneous impression regarding its character, value, quantity, composition, merit or safety." The guide further elaborates, "to advertise means to make any representation to the public by any means whatever for the purpose of promoting directly or indirectly the sale of a product."

Federal and Provincial Acts and Regulations pertaining to agriculture practices and to production, manufacturing, packaging, grading, marketing, storage, importation and exportation of food products may impose additional requirements on advertising, labelling, standardizing and packaging of food. The Trade Marks Act and Combines Investigation Act also have some bearing on advertising and labelling of food. The latter states that for promoting the supply or use of a product for any business interest no person:

a) can make a false or misleading representation
b) can make a statement, warranty or guarantee of performance of a product not based on adequate and proper test, and proof lies upon the person making representation.

In addition, individual approval for radio and television food advertisements is required from a representative of both Consumer and Corporate Affairs Canada and the Canadian Radio-Television Telecommunications Commission. A registration number is then assigned by the Commission. The home economist developing a recipe for written or oral presentation or food photography for such advertisements is not normally involved in making these applications but will need to work within the framework of those requirements.

The guide also states, "the actual words used in an advertisement as well as the impression created by the advertisement are important. The size of displays and the relative size of modifying statements should be appropriate. Words that have no explicit meaning should be avoided. There are no bilingual requirements concerning food advertising, however there are bilingual ones respecting mandatory statements on the labels of prepackaged products. Food should be described in advertisements by its common name. An ingredient should not be given an undue emphasis which might create a false impression concerning the nature or composition of the food". In this area, home economists seek close communication with the client's marketing personnel.

The guide further explains, "it is misleading to overemphasize the importance of an ingredient because of its desirable flavour, well-known nutritional properties, its current popular appeal or any other reasons when it is not present in a food in a significant amount. Adjectives should be factual and accurate. In general, the physical form of the ingredients added to a product does not have to be described in the list of ingredients (e.g. ground, diced, cut, shredded). It is considered unacceptable to use partial truths so as to create a false impression concerning a food. This impression can be created by illustrations as well as words".

Pictures and charts are a common and valuable aid to advertising. They should not however, be used to exaggerate, mislead or misrepresent the value of the product. Where the picture professes to represent the food offered for sale, the actual marketplace product should be shown. The prepared product should also be fairly represented. Illustrations of ingredients which are not present in the food and appear on the label or in advertisement of that food, may be deceptive. Creation of a vague, mysterious, provocative or otherwise unusual atmosphere that has no relation to the product or its origin should be avoided.

Food advertising and labelling are marketing utilities which enable the buyer (consumer) to make an informed choice. Usual purposes of food advertising from the advertiser's point of view are:

- **to attract buyers to their products in order to increase sales**
- **to create goodwill**
- **to improve understanding between his business and the consumer**

Advertisement should therefore, present not only a worthy picture of his firm but also a true picture of the food. Advertisement for a food commits the seller, ethically to provide what is promised. "There should be at least two beneficiaries to every food sale, one of whom is the purchaser."

Reading informative advertisement for foods keeps consumers alert to opportunities for raising their nutritional standard of living. Specific use should not be made however, of Canada's Food Guide when advertising individual foods, as it was not designed for that purpose. Only general references should be made to the Food Guide in advertisements for food. The main purpose of educational advertising should be to inform the public about nutrients in foods, in general.

Food professionals involved in the writing phase of recipe development may wish to have a copy of the Consumer and Corporate Affairs Canada guidelines close at hand for reference. The following two examples of quite general statements may help to indicate this point:

1. Use of the unmodified term "fresh" in describing food, means unfrozen or unpreserved by any method and offered for sale at the earliest possible moment.
2. When used to describe a food, the term "light" usually implies that the food so described is "low-in" a particular substance – generally "calorie-reduced" categories. No objection is taken to the use of the term "light" on labels or in advertisements for foods when certain requirements are met. In advertisements for other foods which do not meet the requirements for calorie-reduced foods, it is considered a violation of Food and Drug Regulations to describe the food as light, unless the designation light is clearly qualified on the label and in advertisements as to the specific aspect of the product that is considered light e.g. colour, texture, body, taste, sugar.

In summary, the guide emphasizes:

"Foods are the items that must be purchased in order to live and therefore, food advertisements, together with labelling should provide sufficient information on which to make informed and sensible choices."

C Food Grades

Federal regulations for grading relate not only to food advertising and labelling, but also set standards for ingredients. Food professionals must be continually aware of modifications or new developments in these regulations.

Grading and inspection of Canadian agricultural food products provide for labelling that accurately lists the contents. Agriculture Canada has established grades for butter, instant milk powder, cheddar cheese, eggs, fresh and processed fruits and vegetables, honey, maple syrup, beef, veal, lamb and poultry. Federal grade standards apply to food exports, to imported foods of a kind produced in Canada and to foods shipped from one province to another.

Some products have been adapted to metric; for others, adaptation is still pending. Either metric or imperial units of measure are found in this section, depending on the product.

Dairy Products

Butter, cheddar cheese, skim milk powder, whole milk powder and partly skimmed milk powder are graded Canada 1 or Canada 2. Butter and cheddar cheese are also graded Canada 3. Canada 1 is generally available at the retail level.

Butter: "Unsalted" butter is marked as such. Creamery butter is available in standard sizes of 125 g, 250 g and 454 g.

Dairy spread, calorie-reduced butter, whey butter, whipped butter and whipped dairy spread are also sold by grade.

Cheese: Prepackaged cheddar is usually marked "Mild" (has aged two to three months); "Medium" (four to five months); or "Old" (nine months or longer).

All prepackaged natural cheese and process cheese sold at the retail level is marked with the percentage of milk fat and moisture by weight and a list of ingredients. Perishable cheeses such as cream or cottage cheese are marked with a "best before" date.

Less common types of cheese are labelled for relative firmness (soft, semisoft, firm and hard) and for ripening characteristics (e.g. unripened fresh, interior ripened and blue veined). Process cheese products are in three categories:

1. **Process** (naming the variety) **Cheese** is essentially natural cheese melted into a homogeneous mass. It contains slightly more water than natural cheese.
2. **Process Cheese Food** and **Process Cheese Spread** usually contain more than one variety of cheese, in varying quantities. They can contain slightly more moisture than process cheese, and milk or skim milk is added as an extender. Process cheese spread has even more moisture and less fat than process cheese food.
3. **Cold Pack Cheese** and **Cold Pack Cheese Food** are made by grinding and mixing one or more varieties of cheese without using heat.

Fruits, vegetables, nuts, prepared or preserved meats or fish may be added to the above cheeses.

Labelling

The percentage of milk fat is declared on cheddar and specialty cheeses, dairy spread, calorie-reduced butter and partly skimmed milk powder.

Eggs

Eggs in the shell are sold by grade in all provinces.

The grade name appears inside a maple leaf symbol for Canada A1, Canada A and Canada B. The maple leaf does not appear on Canada C, which does not reach the retail market.

Grades indicate quality of eggs and should not be confused with size. Only Canada A1 and Canada A are available in different sizes.

Sizes and Weights for Canada A1 and A

Size	Weight of each egg
Extra large	at least 64 g (2¼ ounces)
Large	at least 56 g (2 ounces)
Medium	at least 49 g (1¾ ounces) but less than 56 g (2 ounces)
Small	at least 42 g (1½ ounces) but less than 49 g (1¾ ounces)
Peewee (Canada A only)	less than 42 g (1½ ounces)

Eggs are graded on:
- **weight**
- **cleanliness, soundness and shape of shell**
- **shape and relative position of yolk within egg**
- **size of air cell (a small air cell indicates freshness)**
- **abnormalities**

CANADA A1 eggs are of premium quality. Cartons are marked with an expiry date nine days from date of grading.

CANADA A eggs are practically clean and normal in shape, with sound shells.

CANADA B eggs are good for general cooking and baking where appearance is not vitally important.

CANADA C eggs are suitable for processing into commercially frozen, liquid and dried egg products.

Processed egg products – liquid, frozen or dried egg yolk and albumen – are rarely available at the retail level. Used commercially for baking and in the food industry, they are graded Canada A, Canada B and Canada C.

Fresh Fruits and Vegetables

Most Canadian fruits and vegetables grown in large quantities are sold by grade. Not all provinces require grading of the same fruits and vegetables. To meet federal standards, apples are sized and must be a minimum diameter of 5.6 cm (2¼ in.). If, in some years, growing conditions warrant, a 5 cm (2 in.) minimum diameter may be permitted. (Currently the apple industry uses imperial measure.)

Fresh fruits and vegetables are graded on:
- **uniformity of size and shape**
- **maximum and minimum diameter**
- **minimum length**
- **colour**

- maturity
- freedom from disease, injury
- cleanliness

Asparagus, beets, brussels sprouts, cabbages, carrots, cauliflower, celery, cucumbers (field and greenhouse), head lettuce, onions, parsnips, potatoes and tomatoes (field and greenhouse) are graded Canada No. 1 or Canada No. 2. Celery can also be graded Canada No. 1 Heart; onions, Canada No. 1, Pickling; and potatoes, Canada No. 1 Large and Canada No. 1 Small. Rutabagas and sweet corn are graded Canada No. 1.

Apricots, crabapples, cranberries, grapes, peaches, plums, prunes (prune plums) and rhubarb (field) are graded Canada No. 1 or Canada Domestic. Blueberries, cantaloupes and strawberries are graded Canada No. 1. Cherries are graded Canada No. 1, Canada Domestic, or Canada Orchard Run. Apples and pears are graded Canada Extra Fancy, Canada Fancy, or Canada Commercial (Canada Cee, Canada "C"). Instead of Canada Fancy, pears may be classified as Canada No. 1.

Imports

Fresh fruits and vegetables from the United States, for which grades are established in Canada, are inspected there. Produce from other countries is inspected when it enters Canada. Bulk displays must be marked with the "Canada" grade mark and the country of origin, e.g. Canada No. 1, Product of U.S.A.

Processed Fruits and Vegetables

Only federally registered plants may ship processed fruits and vegetables from one province to another or out of Canada. "Canada" will appear in the grade name.

Imported fruit and vegetable products cannot use "Canada" as part of the grade name when sold in original containers.

Jams, jellies, pie fillings, pickles and similar processed fruit and vegetable products are not sold by grade.

Grades

Processed fruits and vegetables are graded on:
- flavour and aroma
- colour
- tenderness and maturity
- uniformity of size and shape
- consistency of texture
- appearance of liquid (e.g. canned peas)
- freedom from defects and foreign matter

Canned, frozen, dried and dehydrated fruits and vegetables, tomato juice, tomato juice cocktail, mixed vegetable juices and apple juice from concentrate are graded Canada Fancy or Canada Choice. Canned fruits and vegetables may also be classified as Canada Standard.

Grades for Canned Fruits and Vegetables

CANADA FANCY is suitable for use when appearance, uniformity of size and colour are important.

CANADA CHOICE is suitable for general use when perfect uniformity in size and colour are not important.

CANADA STANDARD consists of produce not necessarily of uniform size. Canned fruit of this grade is economical for pudding and sauces. Vegetables may be less tender and are suitable for soups, stews and similar dishes.

Can Sizes

Canned fruits and vegetables are packed in standard containers of 142 mL (5 fl. oz.), 284 mL (10 fl. oz.), 398 mL (14 fl. oz.), 540 mL (19 fl. oz.), 796 mL (28 fl. oz.), 1.36 L (48 fl. oz.) and 2.84 L (100 fl. oz.).

Special sizes are allowed for asparagus, whole kernel and vacuum-packed corn, corn-on-the-cob, fruit and vegetable juices, baby foods, tomato paste and sweet potatoes.

Labelling

Metric-size cans are marked in millilitres only.

Some canned vegetables are size graded and marked with the size or size description.

Sugar added to frozen fruit must be declared on the label as percentage of dry sugar. When fruits are packed without sugar, the words "no sugar added" or "unsweetened" must appear.

Processed Fruit Syrups

Regulations permit a variety of syrup strengths, ranging from extra heavy syrup to slightly sweetened water. Fruit may also be packed in fruit juice without the addition of extra sugar.

There are five syrup strengths which are based on the soluble solids content of the liquid (sugar syrup and juice from the fruit). The five strengths are:

1. Extra heavy syrup or extra heavy fruit juice syrup is used mostly in imported fruit. It has a minimum of 23 percent soluble solids in canned or frozen peaches, pears, pineapple and fruit salad or 25 percent in apples, apricots, berries, cherries and plums.
2. Heavy syrup or heavy fruit juice syrup has a minimum of 18 to 19 percent soluble solids depending on the fruit and is the syrup most often seen on the market.
3. Light syrup or light fruit juice syrup has a minimum of 14 to 15 percent soluble solids.
4. Slightly sweetened water or slightly sweetened fruit juice has a minimum of 10 to 11 percent soluble solids.
5. Fruit packed in its own juice has no extra sugar added.

Frozen Fruits and Vegetables

CANADA FANCY consists of best quality produce. CANADA CHOICE is a good flavoured product but not as perfect in appearance.

Special blends or combination mixed frozen vegetables may contain some vegetables for which grades are not established, and others for which they are. These mixtures are assigned either Canada Fancy or Canada Choice grade.

Dehydrated and Dried Fruits and Vegetables

Standards are established for maximum allowable moisture and preservative content. The dried product contains more moisture than the dehydrated product.

Fruit and Vegetable Juices and Nectars

"Juice" on the label indicates juice only. If salt or sugar is added it must be declared.

Tomato Juice Cocktail consists principally of tomato juice to which is added another vegetable juice.

Mixed Vegetable Juices consists of two or more vegetable juices including tomato juice. Juice names must appear in order of their proportion.

Fruit Nectars contain puréed fruit blended with water or fruit juice. They may contain sugar, citric acid or lemon juice and ascorbic acid.

Juices and nectars with vitamin C added may be packed with or without ascorbic acid. When labelled "vitamin C added" tomato juice cocktail, mixed vegetable juices and grape juice must contain not less than 18 mg ascorbic acid per 100 mL of juice. Apple juice must contain not less than 35 mg ascorbic acid per 100 mL of juice.

Sizes

Fruit and vegetable juices that are graded are packed in the following size containers: 156 mL (5½ fl. oz.), 170 mL (6 fl. oz.), 250 mL (8.8 fl. oz.), 284 mL (10 fl. oz.), 398 mL (14 fl. oz.), 540 mL (19 fl. oz.), 796 mL (28 fl. oz.), 1 L (35.2 fl. oz.), 1.35 L (48 fl. oz.), 2.27 L (80 fl. oz.) and 2.84 L (100 fl. oz.).

Honey

Most honey sold in retail stores is Canada No. 1 and is in liquid or cream form. Colour of honey does not affect grade but is an indication of flavour; usually the darker the honey, the stronger the flavour.

Other grades available include, Canada No. 2 and Canada No. 3 which are used by the bakery trade and for other commercial purposes.

Maple Syrup

Maple syrup is graded on colour, characteristic flavour, freedom from fermentation and cloudiness. The grades are: Canada No. 1, Canada No. 2, and Canada No. 3 (not usually available in retail stores).

When syrup is sold in another province or country, it must be one of the "Canada" grades.

Meat

Health Inspection

All meat destined for interprovincial, foreign or import trade must be health inspected by federal government inspectors. Some provinces have their own regulations for meat sold within their borders.

Composition Standards

During meat processing, the method of preparation, formulae and ingredients must be approved as an additional measure of protection. Percentage of total protein is also regulated. e.g. Regular ground beef must have a minimum of 16 percent total protein and a maximum of 30 percent fat; medium ground beef a maximum of 23 percent fat; and lean ground beef a maximum of 17 percent fat.

Grading

Grading is available to the industry on a voluntary basis. British Columbia, Alberta, Saskatchewan and Ontario have their own regulations using federal grade specifications.

Most beef sold at the retail level is graded and in some areas consumers may buy graded veal and lamb. Pork is not sold by grade in retail stores. There are 10 quality grades for beef, five for veal and four for lamb.

Quality grades for beef, veal and lamb are identified by a coloured ribbon brand – Canada A, red; Canada B, blue; Canada C, brown; and Canada D, black – with various subcategories.

Poultry

Dressed and eviscerated poultry must be graded in most major cities. All eviscerated poultry that is imported, exported or shipped between provinces must be graded and health inspected.

Poultry is graded on:

- **conformation – presence of deformities that affect appearance or normal distribution of flesh (e.g., a crooked keel bone)**
- **fleshing – distribution and amount of flesh in specific areas**
- **fat covering – distribution and amount of fat in specific areas**
- **dressing – presence of defects such as discolouration, tears, pinfeathers, bruises or other blemishes**

Grades

Grade names are the same for chickens, stewing hens, turkeys, ducks and geese. Turkeys, ducks and geese must be marked as "young" or "mature". Poultry grades are Canada A, identified by a red tag and Canada B and Canada Utility, both with blue tags. Canada C, not usually available at retail, has a brown tag.

D Food Labelling

As indicated by Consumer and Corporate Affairs Canada, information required or acceptable on a food label may be used to advertise that food. Labelling data will conveniently provide food professionals with key information for preparing recipes to incorporate special dietary products.

Generally in Canada, Consumer and Corporate Affairs Canada is responsible for the legislation regarding labelling, packaging and advertising of food. Legislation administrated by other departments, (such as the Fish Act administered by Fisheries and Oceans Canada, the Meat Inspection Act and the Canada Agricultural Products Standards Act administered by Agriculture Canada), may have more specific requirements.

According to the Food and Drugs Act and Regulations and the Consumer Packaging and Labelling Act and Regulations, a label applied to a food product must carry:

1. the common name of the food.

2. the identity and principal place of business of the person by or for whom the food was manufactured or produced for resale.

3. a complete list of ingredients by their acceptable common names in descending order of their proportions by weight, unless the quantity of each ingredient is stated in terms of percentages.

Ingredients which appear immediately after the other ingredients, but may be listed in any order, include:

- **spices, seasonings and herbs, except salt**
- **natural and artificial flavours**
- **food additives**
- **vitamins**
- **mineral nutrients**
- **salts of mineral nutrients**

Ingredients which may be listed under a class name rather than their common name, include:

Ingredient	Class Name
Vegetable fats or oils, except cocoa-butter, coconut oil, palm oil or palm kernel oil	*"vegetable oil" or "vegetable fat"*
Marine fats or oils	*"marine oil"*
Permitted food colours	*"colour"*
Natural flavours	*"flavour"*
Artificial flavours	*"artificial flavour", "imitation flavour" or "simulated flavour"*
Spices, seasonings or herbs, except salt	*"spices", "seasonings" or "herbs"*
Any combination of all types of milk: whole skimmed or partly skimmed, cream, butter and butter oil	*"milk solids" or "dairy ingredients"*
Any combination of disodium phosphate, monosodium phosphate, sodium hexametaphosphate, tetra sodium pyrophosphate and sodium acid pyrophosphate	*"sodium phosphate" or "sodium phosphates"*

4. the durable life date and storage instructions, as required.

Packaged foods (except prepackaged fruits, vegetables, and fresh meats, poultry or fish and their by-products) that should be used within 90 days or less must show a durable life date, with the words "best before".

If these products require special storage conditions, instructions for proper storage must be included on the label.

It should be noted that products may be safe to eat after the date; however, there may be a deterioration in quality.

5. the net quantity of the food.

In prepackaged products, with a few exceptions, the net quantity must be by weight for solid products and by volume when the product is liquid or viscous.

All the above information must appear in both French and English, with the exception of the name and address of the manufacturer which may appear in either language. Products which are sold in Quebec must have both languages equally displayed.

In certain cases, other forms of labelling not actually on the product may be legally required. For example, if frozen meat or a meat by-product is thawed before being offered for sale, the words "previously frozen" must appear on the label or on a sign close to where the food is sold.

Universal Product Code Symbol (UPC)

In addition, the UPC symbol almost always appears on food products. This symbol is a series of lines and numbers which code the manufacturer, product source, exact product and related size. Through the checkout counter's electronic scanner, the symbol relays to a computer the name and manufacturer of each product; this information is automatically printed along with the price on a cash register tape. Its use in stores with automated checkout systems speeds customer service, lessens the opportunity for pricing errors and aids inventory control and management. The need for pricing each individual item on the shelf is eliminated but consumers may find price comparisons more difficult. Although not required by law, retail stores can refuse products which are without the symbol.

E *Garnishes*

Garnishes often become an integral part of successful recipe presentation as they are used to enhance or add contrast to the appearance, colour and possibly flavour of a recipe. Just as it adds that finishing touch to a prepared recipe, a garnish suggestion adds appeal to recipe copy.

When choosing garnishes, keep in mind that they must be compatible with the type and overall appearance of the recipe. Originality is desirable; however, garnishes need not be overwhelming. It is important to consider the texture, colour, appearance and flavour characteristics of an item when recommending a garnish.

A garnish is often chosen because it reflects the main flavour of a recipe; a lemon chiffon pie lends itself to a lemon and whipping cream garnish. The actual presentation of these items is limited only by the imagination.

Successful garnishes not only compliment the sensory qualities of a prepared item, they also compliment the occasion, serving dish and end use. For example, a recipe developed for a buffet table may lend itself to more elaborate garnish suggestions than would a similar recipe intended for a picnic setting.

While the list of garnish ideas is virtually unlimited, terminology in recipe copy can sometimes become difficult and redundant. This can be dealt with, to some extent, by avoiding the use of old standards such as "garnish with sprigs of parsley". Terminology is of special importance when developing a series of recipes where similarity in garnish suggestions should always be avoided.

The following list offers suggestions for specific food categories. Through experimentation the home economist will, no doubt, create additional original combinations to meet specific qualities of the recipe she is working with.

Cold Beverages:

- strawberries
- orange, lemon or lime slices
- melon balls
- candy sticks
- scoops of sherbet or ice cream
- mint leaves
- maraschino cherries
- pineapple chunks

Hot Beverages:

- twists of orange, lemon, grapefruit
  or cucumber peel
- cinnamon sticks
- whipped cream
- marshmallows

Salads:

- grated or shredded cheese
- mushroom slices or caps
- asparagus tips
- small onion rings
- cottage cheese scoops
- cucumber twists
- tomato wedges
- pimento
- green onion
- lemon slices
- sour cream
- croutons
- dill sprigs
- chives
- black olives
- cherry tomatoes
- carrot curls
- celery leaves
- watercress
- pickle fan
- endive
- baby beets
- radish rosettes
- sieved egg yolk
- chicory
- crackers

Soups:
- a dollop of sour cream
- bacon bits
- chopped hard-cooked eggs
- chopped green onions or chives
- grated cheese
- grated carrot
- twists of orange, lemon or grapefruit
- croutons
- whipped or sour cream
- sliced cauliflowerets
- chopped mint

Sandwiches:
- raw vegetable sticks
- devilled eggs
- grape clusters
- pickled onions
- pimento strips
- green or red pepper slices
- carrot curls
- raisins
- chopped green onion or chives
- olives
- pickle fan
- tomato wedges
- cheese slices
- spiced crabapples
- parsley
- sliced fresh mushrooms
- orange or grapefruit sections
- dollop of mayonnaise

Cold Salad or Meat Plates:
- vegetable cutouts
- pickle fan
- green or red pepper chain
- grape clusters
- radish tulips
- tomato-peel rose
- cucumber twists
- cherry tomatoes
- watercress
- tomato rose
- shredded raw carrots
- carrot curls
- melon balls
- apple wedges
- avocado or banana slices
- chicory
- orange slices
- celery fans
- cauliflowerets
- green onions

Vegetable Dishes:
- grated or melted cheese
- slivered almonds
- sour cream
- crumbled cooked bacon
- chopped parsley
- flavoured butter, e.g. lemon, herb
- chives
- chopped pimento
- onion slices
- lemon slices

Desserts:
- candied fruit
- marshmallows
- grated chocolate
- maraschino cherries
- orange, lemon or lime twists
- freshly ground nutmeg
- cinnamon sticks
- cookie wedges
- grated fruit peel
- cocoa
- melted chocolate drizzle
- mandarin orange sections
- crushed candy
- mint leaves
- chocolate-dipped fruit
- icing sugar
- sugared grapes
- wafer crumbs
- toasted shredded coconut
- chocolate curls
- toasted slivered almonds
- whole, chopped, or ground nuts
- fresh berries
- fan of fresh fruit slices

F Spices and Herbs

Spice: An aromatic, natural product obtained from the dried seeds, fruit, flower, buds, bark or root of plants that are usually of tropical origin. Frequently available either whole or ground.

Herb: The whole or ground leaves and sometimes the flowers of plants that are usually grown in a temperate climate.

Spices and herbs have long been used to enhance the natural flavour of food. Creative use of one or more of the many available seasonings can contribute to the appetizing aroma, colour and flavour of a meal. A recipe can often take on a new or unusual characteristic simply through the addition of spices and herbs.

"Well seasoned" food is especially appealing because of *controlled* addition of herbs and/or spices. Generally, no particular flavour should predominate or overpower the others. Home economists developing recipes will recommend seasonings in small quantities. It is easier for the consumer to add more spices, dictated by personal preference, than to correct or remove seasonings if too much has been added.

Usually, in recipe development with herbs, the dried or ground version is specified due to limited availability of fresh ones. A useful equivalent is:

2 mL (½ tsp.) GROUND = 5 mL (1 tsp.) DRIED = 15 mL (1 tbsp.) FRESH

A list of herbs and spices, their characteristics and common uses are outlined below.

Characteristic	Common Use
Allspice Available ground or whole; one spice, it resembles a blend of cloves, cinnamon and nutmeg.	*In meat and poultry dishes, pickles, relishes, cakes, cookies, pastries; with beets, squash, carrots, sweet potatoes.*
Anise Seed Seed or ground; aroma and flavour resemble licorice.	*With fruits; in breads, cookies, candies.*
Basil Broken dried leaves or ground; sweet faintly anise-like flavour and aroma.	*In tomato sauces and dishes, soups, stuffings, salad dressings; as garnish for egg, cheese, poultry and tomato dishes; with snap beans, brussels sprouts, cucumbers, peas, potatoes, spinach.*
Bay Leaves Leaves up to 7 cm (3 in.) long or ground.	*In meat and poultry dishes, particularly pot roasts and stews; in fish and vegetable dishes, pickles.*
Caraway Seed Seeds up to 6 mm (¼ in.) long; distinctive aroma and slightly sharp taste.	*In breads, cheese spreads and dips, sauerkraut, sweet pickles; as garnish for breads, cheese, coleslaw; with broccoli, brussels sprouts, cauliflower, onions, carrots, beets.*

Characteristic	Common Use
Cardamom Seed Whole pods with seeds; ground seeds and pod or seeds only. Has pleasant aroma, slightly sharp taste.	*Use whole seeds in demitasse, pickles; ground in cookies, coffee cakes; with fruit, sweet potatoes.*
Celery Seed Seeds; ground and combined with salt (celery salt); dried leaves and some of the stalk of the American celery plant (celery flakes); slightly bitter, fresh-celery flavour.	*In meat, cheese, egg and fish dishes, barbecue sauces, pickles, soups, salad dressings; with cabbage, potatoes, tomatoes.*
Chervil Leaves resembling parsley; has pleasant aroma and flavour resembling tarragon.	*In fish and egg dishes, soups, salads, meat sauces and stews.*
Chili Powder Red to very dark red powder, with characteristic aroma and varying degrees of pungency.	*In meat dishes, (especially Spanish or Mexican-style), pickles, barbecue sauces, cocktail dips, cheese, salad dressings, snack foods; egg, vegetable and seafood dishes.*
Chives Fresh, thin tubular leaves; freeze-dried and chopped; flavour is mild, onion-like.	*In cheese, egg, fish and poultry dishes; soups; with vegetables; as garnish for salads, soups, potatoes.*
Cinnamon Sticks or rolled bark in various lengths, or ground. Flavour and aroma are sweet and pungent.	*In sweet vegetable (squash, sweet potatoes) and fruit dishes, baked beans, pickles, breads, cakes, cookies, desserts.*
Cloves Whole or ground; flavour and aroma are strong, pungent and sweet.	*In meat and poultry dishes, barbecue sauces; with sweet vegetables, pickles, fruits, relishes, breads, cookies, desserts, candies; as garnish for relishes, ham, spiced fruits.*
Coriander Seed Whole or ground; flavour and aroma are distinctively lemon-like.	*In pickles, breads, cookies, cakes.*
Cumin Seed Whole or ground; flavour and aroma are strong and slightly bitter.	*In Spanish and Mexican-style meat and rice dishes; cheese spreads, egg, fish and vegetable dishes.*
Curry Powder A blend of cloves, cardamom, fennel, cumin, nutmeg, mace and turmeric in any combination. Golden in colour; distinctive flavour typical of Indian cooking.	*In meat, poultry, fish, shellfish, egg, cheese and vegetable dishes; sauces, salad dressings, soups.*
Dill Leaves and stems (dill weed) and seeds; flavour and aroma are slightly sharp.	*In pickles, cheese dishes, salad dressings, cocktail dips, fish and shellfish dishes; with beets, brussels sprouts, cabbage, carrots, cauliflower, peas, cucumbers, potatoes. Fresh dill is used to garnish salads, seafood, casseroles.*

Characteristic	Common Use
Fennel Seed Whole or ground; flavour and aroma are sweet, anise-like.	*Breads, Italian-type sauces, fish sauces, pickles; as garnish for baked goods, carrots.*
Ginger Whole, ground or cracked (in small pieces). Crystallized or candied ginger is a confection but may be added in chutneys, baked goods or as a garnish. Flavour and aroma are pungent, sweet; taste is "hot".	*In Oriental-style meat, poultry, seafood and vegetable dishes; in relishes, pickles, salad dressings, breads, cookies, cakes, desserts; with carrots, beets.*
Mace Whole or ground; flavour and aroma of nutmeg but stronger, less delicate.	*In soups, salad dressings, meat and poultry spreads, egg, potato and cheese dishes, baked goods. Particularly good with chocolate.*
Marjoram Dried leaves or ground; distinctive aroma is similar to oregano, flavour slightly bitter.	*In meat, poultry, fish, cheese and egg dishes; vegetable sauces, Italian-style dishes; with lima beans, snap beans, carrots, eggplant, peas, spinach.*
Mint Fresh or dried leaves, and flakes; flavour and aroma are strong and sweet; provides cool after-taste.	*With peas, cucumbers, carrots, cabbage, snap beans, fruits, desserts; in jelly, teas, relishes; as garnish for beverages, desserts.*
Mustard Seed Whole or powdered; yellow seeds have no odour but sharp, pungent taste when combined with water; brown seeds combined with water have sharp irritating odour and pungent taste.	*In pickles and relishes, salad dressings, egg and cheese dishes, cocktail dips, sandwich spreads; with squash, potatoes, onions, cabbage, brussels sprouts, broccoli, beets, snap beans, asparagus.*
Nutmeg Whole seed up to 3 cm (1¼ in.) long, or ground; flavour and aroma are sweet.	*In beverages, sweet potato, squash, spinach, onion, cabbage, carrots, breads, cookies, cakes, desserts; as garnish for beverage, sauces, desserts.*
Oregano Fresh leaves or ground; flavour and aroma are similar to marjoram and thyme but stronger.	*In Italian and Mexican-style main-course foods and sauces; snack foods, cocktail dips, beef, poultry, seafood, cheese and vegetable (especially tomato) dishes.*
Paprika Powder, varying in colour from rich bright red to lighter red; flavour and aroma are slightly sweet; may have slight "bite".	*In meat, poultry and cheese dishes, salad dressings, snack foods; as garnish for cream soups, casseroles, dips, salads.*
Parsley Fresh leaves and stems or dried flakes; flavour and aroma are mild, pleasant.	*In soups, salads, meat, poultry, seafood, cheese, egg and vegetable dishes; as garnish for salads, soups, main dishes.*

Characteristic	Common Use
Pepper Black pepper is available as whole peppercorns, cracked coarsely ground, or ground; white pepper is whole or ground; red pepper is whole pods and ground or crushed. All have hot biting taste and characteristic odour.	*In most foods; soups, main dishes, salads, salad dressings, snack and appetizer foods, pickles. Use red and Cayenne pepper sparingly. Of the peppers, Cayenne is hottest, white is mildest, red varies.*
Poppy Seed Whole; flavour and aroma are sweet, mild, nut-like.	*In noodles, salad dressings, breads, rolls, beef and vegetable dishes, fillings for breads and cakes; as garnish for cheese, snack foods; with peas, potatoes.*
Rosemary Needle-like leaves; ground; flavour and aroma are distinctive, tea-like, bittersweet.	*In meats, poultry and fish dishes, stuffings, breads, salads; as garnish for salads, breads; with peas, squash.*
Saffron Strands 1-2 cm (½-¾ in.) long, or ground; aroma is strong, medicinal; flavour is pleasantly bitter.	*In poultry, fish and shellfish dishes, rice, breads.*
Sage Dried leaves 7 cm (3 in.) long, rubbed or ground; flavour and aroma are slightly bitter.	*In meat, poultry and cheese dishes, stuffings; with lima beans, brussels sprouts, onions, peas, tomatoes.*
Savory Dried leaves or ground; aroma is pine-like.	*In meat, poultry, egg and rice dishes; with lima beans, snap beans, beets, cabbage, peas.*
Sesame Seed Whole; flavour and aroma are slightly nut-like.	*In rolls, breads, snacks, candy; as garnish for breads, snack foods, asparagus, tomatoes.*
Tarragon Dried leaves or ground; flavour and aroma are somewhat astringent.	*In poultry, seafood, cheese, lamb and egg dishes; with salad dressings, asparagus, beans, snap beans, broccoli, cabbage, cauliflower, cucumbers, tomatoes.*
Thyme Dried leaves or ground; flavour is pungent, aroma distinctive.	*In meat, poultry, seafood, egg and cheese dishes; with lima and snap beans, beets, brussels sprouts, onions, potatoes, tomatoes; in soups, stuffings, salad dressings.*
Turmeric Ground; brilliant-yellow in colour, flavour is slightly bitter, aroma pepper-like.	*In pickles, relishes, salad dressings, curries; cheese, egg and fish dishes.*

G General Effects of Altitude on Cooking

Cooking at high altitudes often requires adjustments in cooking times, temperatures and recipe proportions as ingredients and methods are affected by the decline in air pressure. The following guidelines indicate changes which may be required. Further experimentation is necessary to establish precise adjustments.

1. Cooking times for boiled or simmered foods may increase. Water boils 1°C (2°F) lower for each 300 m (1000 feet) increase in altitude; consequently internal heat needed to cook food takes longer to develop.

Approximate Boiling Temperatures of Water at Various Altitudes

Altitude		Boiling Point of Water*	
m	*ft.*	*°C*	*°F*
Sea Level		100.0	212.0
609	2000	98.4	208.4
1 524	5000	95.0	203.0
2 286	7500	92.4	198.4
3 048	10000	90.0	194.0
4 572	15000	85.0	185.0
9 144	30000	70.0	158.0

2. The amount of liquid in boiled or simmered recipes must be increased as it will evaporate more quickly.

3. For deep-fat frying, the temperature of the fat must be lowered by 2°C (3°F) for each 300 m (1000 feet) increase in altitude. Moisture in the food has a lower boiling point, therefore, food fried at temperatures recommended for sea level will be cooked outside but underdone inside.

4. For candies, frostings, syrups and jellies, the temperature when using a candy thermometer is read as 1°C (2°F) lower for every 300 m (1000 feet) above sea level. Syrups are more readily concentrated at high altitudes due to rapid evaporation.

5. Oven temperature is not affected by altitude changes; however, since air pressure decreases at higher altitudes, doughs and batters rise more rapidly. Increasing oven temperature by 15°C (25°F) for altitudes of 1 000 m (3280 feet) and above, will allow cakes to set before the leavening expands too much.

6. Rising times for yeast breads may require decreasing to avoid overproofing.

7. Meat, fruit and vegetable dishes cooked in an oven are not affected by high altitudes.

8. To compensate for the lowered boiling point of water at high altitudes, processing times for canning must be altered. When processing 20 minutes or less, increase total time by one or two minutes for every 300 m (1000 feet) in altitude. When processing more than 20 minutes, increase total time by two minutes for every 300 m (1000 feet) increase in altitude. To raise the boiling point of water, steam pressure must be increased by 3.5 kPa (0.5 psi) for every 300 m (1000 feet) above sea level.

Steam Pressures at Various Altitudes and Temperatures

| Desired Temperature | | Sea Level | | Required Pressure | | | | | |
| | | | | 1 200 m (4000 ft.) | | 1 800 m (6000 ft.) | | 2 100 m (7000 ft.) | |
°C	°F	kPa	psi	kPa	psi	kPa	psi	kPa	psi
109	228	34.5	5	48	7	55	8	58.6	8.5
115	240	69	10	83	12	90	13	93.1	13.5
121	250	103	15	117	17	124	18	127.6	18.5

9. The proportion of leavenings, liquids and sugar in baked goods are most affected by lowered air pressure. With less air pressure to control expansion, baked products rise too quickly, evaporation is accelerated and foods become dry and crumbly. As liquids evaporate, sugars become more concentrated and the cell structure is weakened, causing cakes to fall. Fats will also weaken cell structure. "Rich" cakes may need less fat (15-25 mL per 250 mL/1-2 tbsp. per cup). Conversely, since eggs strengthen cell structure, adding an egg may prevent "rich" cakes from falling. Cakes which rely largely on air for leavening (angel food, sponge) expand too much if egg whites are beaten excessively; beat them only until soft peaks form.
The following table provides a general guideline for altering ingredient proportions in cakes. When two amounts are given, experiment first with the smaller.

Adapting Cake Recipes for High Altitudes

| Ingredient | Adjustment Required | | |
	1 000 m (3280 ft.)	1 500 m (4921 ft.)	2 000 m (6561 ft.)
LIQUID: For every 250 mL (1 cup) ADD	15-30 mL (1-2 tbsp.)	30-60 mL (2-4 tbsp.)	45-60 mL (3-4 tbsp.)
BAKING POWDER: For every 5 mL (1 tsp.) DECREASE	0.5 mL (⅛ mL)	0.5-1 mL (⅛-¼ tsp.)	1-2 mL (¼-½ tsp.)
SUGAR: For every 250 mL (1 cup) DECREASE	0-15 mL (0-1 tbsp.)	0-30 mL (0-2 tbsp.)	15-45 mL (1-3 tbsp.)

Recipes calling for baking soda may also require a slight reduction.

H Fats, Oils and Shortenings

Although an oil is a fat, it is common practice to use the term "fat" only for those in a solid state when at room temperature (generally animal fats). Fats which are liquid at room temperature are called oils (generally vegetable fats). Shortening is referred to as a fat because it is solid at room temperature; it is animal and/or vegetable oils which have been made solid through hydrogenation. A shortening or oil without "pure" in its definition has additives to lengthen storage life or improve cooking properties.

To successfully deep-fry foods, (fat) oil temperatures must be raised, but it is important to stay below the smoke point for that specific (fat) oil.

The smoke point is reached when fats are heated to a temperature where decomposition occurs and visible fumes are given off. Although fats vary in temperature at which smoking begins, those that start smoking at low temperatures are not always appropriate for frying due to the odour and irritating effect of the fumes. An unpleasant flavour may be produced as a result of decomposition. Reaching the smoke point can be hazardous since it indicates proximity to the burn point.

A number of factors will decrease the smoke point of any fat:
- **combination of vegetable oils in product**
- **presence of foreign properties (batter)**
- **temperature to which oil is heated**
- **presence of salt**
- **number of times oil is used**
- **length of time oil is heated**
- **storage of oil (exposure to oxygen, light, temperature)**

Smoke Points of Fats and Oils

Ingredient	Temperature	
	°C	°F
lards	183-205	361-401
vegetable oils (non specific)	227-232	441-450
safflower	265	510
soybean	260	495
corn	250	475
peanut	225	440
sesame	215	420
olive	190	375
vegetable shortenings with emulsifier	180-188	356-370
vegetable and animal shortenings		
with emulsifiers	177-184	351-363
without emulsifiers	231	448

Equivalents for Butter

In some instances, it may be appropriate to consider the substitution of various fats or oils, such as margarine or vegetable shortening for butter. Substitution may be made to improve/alter the flavour, or to attract consumers who show a preference for these products. Alternately, it may be desirable to substitute butter for commonly used fats and oils when developing recipes.

When substituting shortening for butter, it is not possible to substitute on a weight for weight basis. As shortening contains more oil than butter on an equal basis, use 15-20 percent less shortening than butter. Because of the air incorporated into shortening, it is possible to substitute on a measure for measure basis. Since oils are 100 percent fat, amounts must be reduced by about 20 percent when substituting either by weight or measure.

Not all recipes calling for butter lend themselves to substitutions. Oils should not be interchanged with butter for baking purposes, since oil cannot be creamed to hold air.

Key Temperatures Related to Food Sanitation

Recipe methods must constantly reflect attention to basic principles of food sanitation. This scale outlines temperature ranges between freezing levels and the boiling point of water which have particular significance for safe handling of food.

At various temperature levels time factors can be significant. For example, raw meat must be used within five days, ground meat, poultry and fish within two days, even if they have been held at a consistent acceptable refrigeration temperature. These temperatures have ranges – optimum, practical and probable – related to factors such as quantity of food stored, frequency and length of time door is open.

The nature of the food product must also be taken into account in selection of storage, holding or cooking temperatures. While it may seem best to store all perishables at refrigerator temperatures or below, this is not always best for the maintenance of desirable quality. Bananas are one type of food that keep better if stored at 13-17°C (55-63°F) rather than refrigerator temperatures.

A Food Sanitation Thermometer

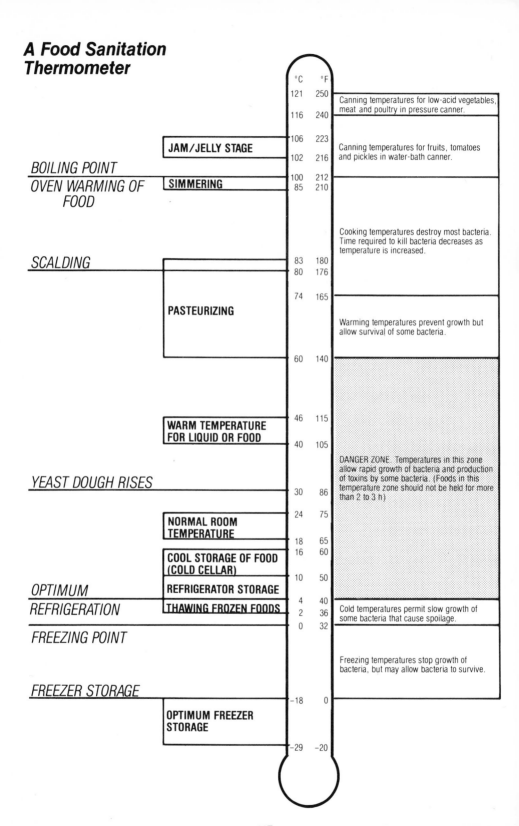

°C | °F

JAM/JELLY STAGE — 106 / 223, 102 / 216

BOILING POINT

OVEN WARMING OF FOOD — **SIMMERING** — 100 / 212, 85 / 210

SCALDING — 83 / 180, 80 / 176

PASTEURIZING — 74 / 165

60 / 140

WARM TEMPERATURE FOR LIQUID OR FOOD — 46 / 115, 40 / 105

YEAST DOUGH RISES — 30 / 86

NORMAL ROOM TEMPERATURE — 24 / 75, 18 / 65

COOL STORAGE OF FOOD (COLD CELLAR) — 16 / 60

REFRIGERATOR STORAGE — 10 / 50

OPTIMUM

REFRIGERATION — **THAWING FROZEN FOODS** — 4 / 40, 2 / 36

FREEZING POINT — 0 / 32

FREEZER STORAGE — −18 / 0

OPTIMUM FREEZER STORAGE — −29 / −20

121 / 250, 116 / 240

Canning temperatures for low-acid vegetables, meat and poultry in pressure canner.

Canning temperatures for fruits, tomatoes and pickles in water-bath canner.

Cooking temperatures destroy most bacteria. Time required to kill bacteria decreases as temperature is increased.

Warming temperatures prevent growth but allow survival of some bacteria.

DANGER ZONE. Temperatures in this zone allow rapid growth of bacteria and production of toxins by some bacteria. (Foods in this temperature zone should not be held for more than 2 to 3 h)

Cold temperatures permit slow growth of some bacteria that cause spoilage.

Freezing temperatures stop growth of bacteria, but may allow bacteria to survive.

] Traditional Ingredient Proportions In Basic Recipes

The following table shows proportions of ingredients to one another in certain basic recipes. The amounts of ingredients may vary somewhat and do not constitute completed recipes. This data is most applicable for quantity recipes. *

Product	Flour**	Liquid	Fat	Eggs	Sugar	Salt	Baking Powder***	Other Ingredients
Beverages								
Cocoa and chocolate		1 c†/250 mL milk (242 g)			2 tsp. - 1 tbsp./ 10-15 mL (8.3-12.5 g)			1 tbsp./15 mL cocoa (7 g) OR ½ oz. (14.2 g) chocolate
Coffee ground		¾ c/175 mL water (178 g)						1 tbsp./15 mL coffee (5.3 g)
instant		¾ c/175 mL water (178 g)						1 tsp./5 mL instant coffee (0.8 g) OR ⅔ tsp./ 3 mL freeze dried coffee (0.5 g)
Tea		¾ c/175 mL water (178 g)						½-1 tsp./ 2-5 mL tea (0.75-1.5 g)
Breads								
Biscuits	1 c/250 mL (115 g)	⅓-½ c/ 75-125 mL milk (80.7-121 g)	2-4 tbsp./ 25-50 mL (23.6-47.2 g)			½ tsp./2 mL††. (3 g)	1¼-2 tsp./ 6-10 mL (4.5-5.8 g)	

Product	Flour**	Liquid	Fat	Eggs	Sugar	Salt	Baking Powder***	Other Ingredients
Muffins	1 c/250 mL (115 g)	1/2 c/125 mL milk (121 g)	2-3 tbsp./ 25-50 mL (23.6-35.4 g)	1/2 (25 g)	1-2 tbsp./ 15-25 mL (12.5-25 g)	1/2 tsp./2 mL (3 g)	1 1/4-2 tsp./ 6-10 mL (4.5-5.8 g)	
Pancakes	1 c/250 mL (115 g)	3/4-7/8 c/ 175-225 mL milk (181.5-211.8 g)	1 tbsp./15 mL (11.8 g)	1/2 (25 g)	0-1 tbsp./ 0-15 mL (0-12.5 g)	1/2 tsp./2 mL (3 g)	1 1/2-2 tsp./ 7-10 mL (5.4-5.8 g)	
Waffles	1 c/250 mL (115 g)	3/4-1 c/ 175-250 mL milk (181.5-242 g)	1-3 tbsp./ 15-50 mL (11.8-35.4 g)	1-2 (50-100 g)		1/2 tsp./2 mL (3 g)	1 1/4-2 tsp./ 6-10 mL 4.5-5.8 g)	
Yeast bread	1 c/250 mL (115 g)	1/3 c/75 mL milk (80.7 g)	0-1 tbsp./ 0-15 mL (0-11.8 g)		1 tsp.-1 tbsp./ 5-15 mL (4.2-12.5 g)	1/4 tsp./1 mL (1.5 g)		1/4 compressed yeast cake (12.8 g) OR 1/4 small package active dry yeast (1.7 g)
Cakes and Pastry Cake with fat	1 c/250 mL cake OR all purpose (96 or 115 g)	1/4-1/2 c/ 50-125 mL milk (60.5-121 g)	2-4 tbsp./ 25-50 mL (23.6-47.2 g)	1/2-1 (25-50 g)	1/2-3/4 c/ 125-175 mL (100-150 g)	1/8-1/4 tsp./ 0.5-1 mL (0.75-1.5 g)	1-2 tsp./5-10 mL (3.6-5.8 g)	flavouring
Chiffon	1 c/250 mL cake (96 g)	1/3 c/75 mL water (79 g)	1/4 c/50 mL salad oil (52.5 g)	3 (150 g)	2/3 c/150 mL (134 g)	1/2 tsp./2 mL (3 g)	1 1/4-1 1/2 tsp./ 6-7 mL (4.5-5.4 g)	1/4 tsp./1 mL cream of tartar (0.8 g). flavouring
Cake without fat (angel)	1 c/250 mL cake (96 g)			1-1 1/2 c/ 250-375 mL whites (246-369 g)	1 1/4-1 1/2 c/ 300-375 mL (250-300 g)	1/2 tsp./2 mL (3 g)		3/4-1 1/2 tsp./ 4-7 mL cream of tartar (2.3-4.6 g), flavouring
Sponge	1 c/250 mL cake (96 g)	0-3 tbsp./50 mL water (0-44.4 g)		5-6 (250-300 g)	1 c/250 mL (200 g)	1/2 tsp./2 mL (3 g)		0-3/4 tsp./ 0-4 mL cream of tartar (0-2.3 g), flavouring

Product	Flour**	Liquid	Fat	Eggs	Sugar	Salt	Baking Powder***	Other Ingredients
Cream puffs	1 c/250 mL (115 g)	1 c/250 mL water (237 g)	½ c/125 mL (144 g)	4 (200 g)		¼ tsp./1 mL (1.5 g)		
Doughnuts	1 c/250 mL (115 g)	¼ c/50 mL milk (60.5 g)	1-1½ tsp./ 5-7 mL (3.9-5.9 g)	½ (25 g)	¼ c/50 mL (50 g)	¼ tsp./1 mL (1.5 g)	1-2 tsp./5-10 mL (3.6-5.8 g)	flavouring
Pastry	1 c/250 mL (115 g)	2 tbsp./25 mL water (29.6 g)	4-5 tbsp./ 50-75 mL (47.2-58.8 g)			½ tsp./2 mL (3 g)		
Egg Recipes Custards		1 c/250 mL milk (242 g)		1-1⅔ (50-83.5 g)	1½-3 tbsp./ 25-50 mL (18.8-37.5 g)	⅛ tsp./0.5 mL (0.75 g)		flavouring
Omelettes		1 tbsp./15 mL milk (15.1 g)		1 (50 g)		⅛ tsp./0.5 mL (0.75 g)		seasonings
Soufflés (entrée)†††	3-4 tbsp./ 50 mL (21.6-28.8 g)	1 c/250 mL milk (242 g)	3-4 tbsp./ 50 mL (35.2-47.2 g)	3 (150 g)		¼-½ tsp./ 1-2 mL (1.5-3 g)		seasonings
Gelatine Recipes Plain jellies and whips		2 c/500 mL milk (484 g), water, fruit juices or other liquids			2 tbsp./25 mL (25 g)			1 envelope gelatine (1 tbsp., 7-10 g)
Fruit or vegetable jellies		3 c/750 mL milk (726 g), water, fruit juices or other liquids			¼ c/50 mL (50 g)	few grains		2 envelopes gelatine (2 tbsp., 14-20 g)

Product	Flour**	Liquid	Fat	Eggs	Sugar	Salt	Baking Powder***	Other Ingredients
Bavarian Creams		2 c./500 mL milk (484 g)		4 (200 g)	1/4 c./50 mL (50 g)			2 envelopes gelatine (2 tbsp., 14-20 g), 2 c./500 mL fruit pulp (484 g), 1 c./250 mL whipping cream (242 g), flavouring
Sponges		3 c./750 mL fruit juices (741 g)		2-4 (100-200 g)	1/4 c./50 mL (50 g)			2 envelopes gelatine (2 tbsp., 14-20 g), flavouring
Puddings Cornstarch		1 c./250 mL milk (242 g)		0-1 (0-50 g)	2-3 tbsp./ 25-50 mL (25-37.5 g)	1/8 tsp./0.5 mL (0.75 g)		1-1½ tbsp./ 15-25 mL cornstarch (8-12 g), flavouring
Rice (baked)		1 c./250 mL milk (242 g)			1 tbsp./15 mL (12.5 g)	few grains		1 tbsp./15 mL raw rice (11.4 g), flavouring
Rice (steamed)		1 c./250 mL milk (242 g)			1-2 tbsp./ 15-25 mL (12.5-25 g)	1/8 tsp./0.5 mL (0.75 g)		2-4 tbsp./ 25-50 mL raw rice (22.8-45.5 g), flavouring
Sauces, Gravies° White sauce thin	1 tbsp./15 mL (7.8 g)	1 c./250 mL milk (242 g)	1 tbsp./15 mL (11.8 g)			1/4 tsp./1 mL (1.5 g)		alternate to flour = 1 tsp./5 mL cornstarch (2.7 g), seasonings, if desired

Product	Flour**	Liquid	Fat	Eggs	Sugar	Salt	Baking Powder***	Other Ingredients
medium	2 tbsp./25 mL (15.6 g)	1 c/250 mL milk (242 g)	2 tbsp./25 mL (23.6 g)			¼ tsp./1 mL (1.5 g)		alternate to flour = 2 tsp./10 mL cornstarch (5.3 g), seasonings, if desired
thick	3-4 tbsp./50 mL 23.4-31.2 g)	1 c/250 mL milk (242 g)	3 tbsp./50 mL (35.4 g)			¼ tsp./1 mL (1.5 g)		alternate to flour = 1 tbsp./15 mL cornstarch (8 g), seasonings if desired
Fruit sauce		1 c/250 mL fruit juice (247 g)			2-4 tbsp./ 25-50 mL (25-50 g)	few grains		¾-1 tbsp./ 10-15 mL cornstarch (6-8 g), fruit, if desired
Soup Cream soups with non-starchy vegetables	1 tbsp./15 mL (7.8 g)	1 c/250 mL milk (242 g)	1 tbsp./15 mL (11.8 g)			¼ tsp./1 mL (1.5 g)		alternate to flour = 1 tsp./5 mL cornstarch (2.7 g), seasonings, vegetables
Cream soups with starchy vegetables	1½ tsp./7 mL (3.7 g)	1 c/250 mL milk (242 g)	1 tbsp./15 mL (11.8 g)			¼ tsp./1 mL (1.5 g)		alternate to flour = ½ tsp./2 mL cornstarch (1.3 g), seasonings, vegetables

* Metric replacement values are based on hard metric conversion.

** All-purpose flour unless cake flour is specified.

*** Use the smaller amount with SAS-phosphate powder (double acting) and the larger amount with tartrate powder or phosphate (quick acting).

† c abbreviates cup due to space limitations.

†† Salt combines 1/2-1 tsp./2-4 mL (3-6 g) with 1 c/250 mL (115 g) flour
1 1/4 tsp./15.5 mL (7.5 g) with 1 lb. (450 g) meat
1/2 tsp./2 mL (3 g) with 1 c/250 mL (237 g) water (for cooked cereal)

††† The thick sauce is a paste when cold. Alternate for 4 tbsp./50 mL (31.2 g) flour is 4 tsp./20 mL (10.7 g) cornstarch. This sauce is used in making mixtures for croquettes, soufflés, blanc manges and similar puddings.

º If liquid is not milk, a little less liquid or a little more starch may be required to balance the percentage of solids present and obtain equivalent thickening.

Thickening and Gelling Agents

Agent	Characteristics and Usage	Basic Preparation Method	Factors Affecting Gel/Thickening
Cornstarch	• Forms a paste. • Cornstarch paste is more translucent than flour paste. • Used in cooked products that require a translucent thickener (e.g. sweet and sour sauce).	• Before adding hot liquid or heating, predisperse starch in fat, cold water or mix with sugar. • Heat to 90°C (194°F) or greater to obtain maximum thickening. • Viscosity increases on cooking. • Stir while cooking.	• Heating with acid causes thinning of paste. • High sugar concentrations retard gelatinization and reduce thickening power.
Egg	• Forms a set gel or thickened paste. • Baked custard has a firm, set structure. • Stirred custard is soft, thickened but not set. • Used to thicken sauces, soups and prepare custard fillings/desserts. • Contributes significant nutritional value.	• Blend well with sugar and milk. • Coagulate by slow heating. • Stir soft custard/sauce while cooking.	• Sugar and dilution raise coagulation temperature. • Acids lower coagulation temperature. • If water is substituted for milk in preparation, a flocculent precipitate forms rather than a gel or paste.
Flour	• Forms an opaque paste. • Used to thicken sauces and stews.	• Before adding hot liquid or heating predisperse in fat, cold liquid or mix with sugar. • Stir while cooking. • Heat to 90°C (194°F) or above to obtain maximum thickening. • Viscosity increases with cooling.	• Heating with acid causes thinning. • High sugar concentrations reduce thickening power.
Gelatine	• Forms a set gel that is firm, springy and quivery. • Gel is transparent. • Used for refrigerated products.	• Before adding hot liquid, predisperse granules in cold liquid or mix with sugar. • Dissolve by heating to 40°C (104°F) or by adding hot liquid. • Stir while dissolving granules. • Chill gelatine mixture to set gel. • Gel will begin to soften at 26.5°C (80°F).	• Heating with an acid and dilution reduces gel strength. • Fresh pineapple, kiwi fruit, papaya and figs contain an enzyme that will prevent gelling.

Agent	Characteristics and Usage	Basic Preparation Method	Factors Affecting Gel/Thickening
Tapioca	• Forms transparent, non-homogeneous paste (tapioca granules remain distinct). • Used for fruit pie fillings, soups and milk puddings. • Contributes some nutritional value.	• For preparation of milk pudding, mix tapioca with cold or hot liquid (no soaking or predispersing is necessary). • Stir while cooking. • Bring just to boil. • Mixture thickens as tapioca particles swell and become transparent. • Viscosity increases on cooling.	• Over-stirring while cooking disrupts tapioca particles, resulting in a sticky gelatinous mixture.

L Cooking Time Guidelines

NOTE: The following charts are estimates of cooking times. Certain factors affect the exact cooking times of various foods, especially meat.

Some recipes in stating oven temperatures give the degrees and then a descriptive term, e.g. 200°C (hot) oven. The following chart outlines commonly accepted descriptive terms for each temperature range in degrees Celsius and Fahrenheit.

1. Descriptive Terms for Oven Temperatures

Temperature		Commonly Accepted Descriptive Term
°C	°F	
120	250	Very Low / Slow
130	275	
150	300	Low / Slow
160	325	
180	350	Moderate
190	375	
200	400	Hot
220	425	
230	450	Very Hot
250	475	
260	500	Extremely Hot
280	525	

2. Approximate Baking Times in Preheated Oven

Food	Time (min)	Temperature °C	°F
BREAD			
Corn	30	190-200	375-400
Fruit & nut	60	180	350
Muffins	30	200	400
Popovers	15	230	450
	then 15-20	at 180	at 350
Tea Biscuits	12-15	230	450
Yeast Loaves	30	190-230	375-450
Yeast Rolls	15-20	180-230	350-450

Food	Time (min)	Temperature °C	°F
CAKES			
Angel	30	190	375
Butter – layer	25-30	180	350
– square	50-60	180	350
Cake Mixes	30-35	180	350
Chiffon	60	160	325
Cupcakes	20-25	180	350
Fruit	1½-4 h	130-150	275-300
Gingerbread	50-60	160-180	325-350
Jelly Roll	15	160	325
Pound	1-1¼ h	160	325
Sponge	60	160	325
Upside Down	50	180	350
COOKIES			
Drop	8-12	180	350
Macaroons	8-10	180	350
Meringues	1 h	100	200
Then turn oven off and leave meringues in oven for at least 4 h.			
Refrigerator	8-10	180	350
Rolled	8-10	190	375
Shaped	10-12	180	350
EGG, MEAT, MILK AND CHEESE DISHES			
Cheese Soufflé, Custards (baked in pan of hot water)	30-60	180	350
Macaroni & Cheese	25-30	180	350
Meatloaf	60-90	180	350
Meat Pie	25-30	200	400
Rice Pudding (uncooked rice)	2-2½ h	150	300
Scalloped Potatoes	1 h	180	350
PASTRY			
Cream Puffs	20	220	425
	then 10-15	at 160	at 325
Double Crust Pie	10	230	450
	then 30-40	at 180	at 350
Eclairs	20	220	425
	then 10-15	at 160	at 325
Pie Shells	10-12	230	450
Tart Shells	10-15	230	450
Turnovers	10	230	450
	then 30-40	at 190	at 375

3. Roasting Temperature and Time Chart

Consideration is given to three important variables when using the roasting time and temperature chart.

1. The most significant factor in cooking meat involves the thickness of the meat. Long, narrow roasts take less time to cook than spherical ones. Allowances are made for the amount of meat and bone. A bone-in or lean piece of meat cooks faster than a boneless or fatty one.
2. The temperature of the meat when placed in an oven and the preheated temperature of the oven also influence cooking.
3. Lastly, the size of the piece of meat will affect cooking. When making adjustments remember, although larger pieces take longer to cook, they require fewer minutes per pound than do smaller pieces.

Cut	Approximate Weight		Thermometer Reading on Removal From Oven		Approximate Cooking Time at 160°C (325°F)
	kg	lb.	°C	°F	h
BEEF					
Rib Roast	2-2.5	4-6	60	140 (rare)	2¼-2¾
			70	160 (medium)	2¾-3¼
			75	170 (well-done)	3¼-3½
Rib Roast	2.5-3.5	6-8	60	140	2½-3
			70	160	3-3½
			75	170	3¾-4
Boneless Rib Roast	2-3	5-7	60	140	3¼-3½
			70	160	3¾-4
			75	170	4½-4¾
Boneless Rolled Rump Roast	2-2.5	4-6	65-75	150-170	2-2½
Tip Roast	1.5-2	3½-4	60-75	140-170	2-2¾
Rib Eye Roast (Delmonico) (roast at 180°C/350°F)	2-2.5	4-6	60	140	1½-1¾
			70	160	1¾
			75	170	2
Tenderloin Roast (roast at 220°C/ 425°F)	2-2.5	4-6	60	140	¾-1
VEAL					
Leg Roast	2-3.5	5-8	75	170	2¾-3¾
Loin Roast	2-2.5	4-6	75	170	2½-3
Boneless Shoulder Roast	2-2.5	4-6	75	170	3½-3¾

Cut	Approximate Weight		Thermometer Reading on Removal From Oven		Approximate Cooking Time at 160°C (325°F)
	kg	lb.	°C	°F	h
FRESH PORK					
Loin Centre Roast	1-2	3-5	75	170	2½-3
Sirloin Roast	2-3	5-7	75	170	3½-4¼
Loin Blade Roast	1-2	3-4	75	170	2¼-2¾
Boneless Top Loin Roast	1-2	3-4	75	170	2½-3
Blade *Boston Roast*	2-2.5	4-6	75	170	3-4
Arm *Picnic*	2-3.5	5-8	75	170	3-4
Leg *(fresh ham)*	4.5-7.5	10-16	75	170	4½-6
Leg, half *(fresh ham)*	2-3	5-7	75	170	3½-4½
SMOKED PORK					
Ham *(cook before eating)*					
whole	4.5-6	10-14	70	160	3½-4
half	2-3	5-7	70	160	2½-3
shank or rump	1-2	3-4	70	160	2-2½
Picnic Shoulder	2-3.5	5-8	75	170	3-4
Ham *(fully cooked when purchased)*					
whole	4.5-6	10-14	60	140	2½-3
half	2-3	5-7	60	140	1¾-2¼
whole, boneless	3.5-4.5	8-10	60	140	2-2¼
half, boneless	2	4-5	60	140	1½-2
LAMB					
Boneless Shoulder	3-5	1-2	70	160 (medium)	1¾-3
Leg, whole	2-3	5-7	60	140 (rare)	1¾-2¼
			70	160 (medium)	2-3
			75-80	170-180 (well-done)	2½-3½
Leg, half	1-2	3-4	70	160 (medium)	1¼-1¾
Square Cut Shoulder	2-2.5	4-6	70	160	1¾-2½

4. Vegetable Cookery Chart

Variety in preparation methods will promote vegetable popularity. Minimum cooking encourages use of fresh, crisp vegetables, highest in nutrients. Some consumers may also like suggestions for unusual "edible wilds".

Unless otherwise specified, time refers to cooking whole vegetables. Times will vary according to vegetable size.

Vegetable	Preparation	Cooking Methods
Artichokes	Wash; trim stems; cut off 3 cm (1 in.) of top. Remove loose outer leaves; snip off sharp leaf tips. Brush lemon juice on cut edges.	Simmer 20-30 min or until leaf pulls out easily. Steam 30-40 min.
Asparagus	Wash; trim scales if stalks are gritty. Break off woody bases where spears snap easily.	Simmer 10-15 min or 8-10 min (cut up). Steam 30-40 min. Pan-sauté 5-8 min.
Beans, green and wax	Wash; remove ends and strings.	Cook until tender-crisp. Simmer 10-20 min whole or cut up; 5-12 min French-style. Steam 20-30 min. Pan-sauté 5-8 min.
Beets	Cut off root and all but 3 cm (1 in.) of stems. Wash. Do not peel whole beets.	Cook until tender. Simmer 35-50 min. Cool slightly; slip off skins. Simmer sliced or cubed beets, 15-20 min (peel first). Pan-sauté 10 min.
Broccoli	Wash; remove outer leaves and tough part of stalks.	Cook until tender-crisp. Simmer 10-15 min. Steam 20-30 min. Pan-sauté 5-7 min.
Brussels sprouts	Trim stems. Remove wilted leaves; wash. To speed cooking cut an X in stem end.	Cook until tender-crisp. Simmer 10-15 min. Steam 20-25 min.
Cabbage	Remove wilted outer leaves; wash. Quarter and remove centre core.	Cook until tender. Boil uncovered for first few minutes; simmer covered for 10-12 min; 3-10 min for shredded cabbage. Steam 10-20 min. Pan-sauté 5-8 min.
Carrots, large	Wash; trim and peel or scrub.	Cook just until tender. Simmer 15-20 min; 10-20 min cut up. Steam 20-30 min. Pan-sauté 5-8 min.

Vegetable	Preparation	Cooking Methods
Carrots, baby	Wash; do not peel.	*Cook just until tender.* *Simmer 5-10 min.* *Steam 10-20 min.* *Pan-sauté 5 min.*
Cauliflower	Wash. Remove leaves and woody stem. Leave whole or break into flowerets.	*Cook just until tender. Simmer 10-20 min (depending on size), 8-15 min for flowerets.* *Steam 15-30 min.* *Pan-sauté 5-7 min (flowerets).*
Celery	Cut off leaves; wash. Separate stalks. Trim root.	*Simmer 6-10 min, 3-5 min cut up.* *Steam 10-15 min cut up.* *Pan-sauté 3-5 min cut up.*
Corn, cobs	Remove husks and silks. Rinse.	*Simmer until tender 6-8 min.*
kernels	Cook cobs. With sharp knife cut kernels from cob.	
Eggplant	Wash; cut off cap. Peel, if desired. Dice or slice.	*For best results pan-sauté in hot oil for about 2 min per side.* *Simmer 5-10 min.* *Bake 30 min at 180°C (350°F).*
Mushrooms	Rinse gently, pat dry. Leave whole, chop, or slice through cap and stem.	*For best results add to small amount of melted butter in skillet. Cover and cook slowly about 10 min; 5 min sliced (stir occasionally).* *Broil 4-5 min (brush with butter).*
Onions	Peel; cut off ends. Leave small onions whole.	*Cook until tender. Simmer 15-20 min.* *Steam 25-35 min.* *Pan-sauté 10-15 min.* *Bake 45-60 min at 180°C (350°F).*
Parsnips	Wash; peel or scrape.	*Cook just until tender.* *Simmer 20-35 min cut up.* *Steam 15-20 min cut up.*
Peas,	Shell and wash.	*Cook just until tender.* *Simmer 8-12 min.* *Steam 15-25 min.* *Pan-sauté 5 min.*
snow	Remove stem; rinse. Do not shell.	*Cook until crisp-tender. Same cooking time as shelled peas.*
Potatoes,	Scrub thoroughly; remove eyes. When possible, cook with skin to save nutrients. When baking, prick unpeeled potatoes.	*Simmer until tender 25-40 min; 15-25 min quartered.* *Bake 50-60 min at 200°C (400°F).*
new	Gently wash skins.	*Simmer until tender 10-15 min.*

Vegetable	Preparation	Cooking Methods
Potatoes, sweet (yams)	Scrub skins. Cut off woody portions. Peel, or cook in jackets, depending on use.	*Bake for 50-70 min at 200°C (400°F) depending on size. Simmer 30-40 min.*
Rutabagas (yellow turnips)	Wash; peel. Slice or cube.	*Cook just until tender. Simmer 20-35 min; 10-20 min cut up. Steam 25-40 min. Pan-sauté 5-8 min cut up.*
Spinach	Remove coarse stems. Wash twice in lukewarm water, discarding water each time.	*Boil, covered in very small amount of water. Reduce heat when steam forms. Turn with fork frequently. Cook 3-5 min after steam forms. Pan-sauté 5-6 min.*
Squash, winter (acorn, buttercup, butternut, hubbard, banana, spaghetti)	Wash; cut in half; remove seeds and strings. For mashing, peel, dice and steam.	*Bake at 180°C (350°F) for 45-90 min. until tender. Simmer 15 min. Steam 35 min.*
summer (vegetable, marrow, zucchini)	Prepare and cook as zucchini (below).	
Tomatoes	Wash; remove stems. Peel. Cut up or cook whole.	*Simmer slowly (10-15 min) without water in tightly covered pan.*
Turnips	Wash; peel. Slice or cube.	*Cook just until tender. Simmer 20-35 min; 10-20 min cut up. Steam 25-40 min. Pan-sauté 5-8 min cut up.*
Zucchini	Wash; do not peel. Cut off ends. Slice.	*Cook until tender-crisp. Simmer 5-10 min sliced. Steam 5-10-min sliced. Pan-sauté 3-5 min sliced.*

5. Temperatures for Deep-Fat Frying

Product	Temperature of Fat (°C)	(°F)
Chicken	175	350
Doughnuts, fish, fritters	175-190	350-375
Croquettes, onions, eggplant	190-195	375-380
French fried potatoes	190	375

6. Temperatures and Tests for Syrup and Candies

Product	Temperature of Syrup at Sea level* (Indicating Concentration Desired)	Test	Test Description
Syrup	110°C (110-112) 230°F (230-234)	Thread	Syrup spins a 5 cm (2 in.) thread when dropped from fork or spoon.
Fondant **Fudge** **Panocha**	115°C (112-115) 239°F (234-239)	Soft ball	Syrup, when dropped into very cold water forms a soft ball which flattens on removal from water.
Caramel	120°C (118-120) 248°F (245-248)	Firm ball	Syrup when dropped into very cold water, forms a firm ball which does not flatten on removal from water.
Divinity **Marshmallows** **Popcorn balls**	125°C (121-130) 257°F (250-266)	Hard ball	Syrup, when dropped into very cold water, forms a ball which is hard enough to hold its shape, yet plastic.
Butterscotch **Taffies**	140°C (132-143) 284°F (270-290)	Soft crack	Syrup, when dropped into very cold water separates into threads which are hard but not brittle.
Brittle **Glaze**	150°C (149-154) 302°F (300-309)	Hard crack	Syrup, when dropped into very cold water, separates into threads which are hard and brittle.

*Cook the syrup about 1°C (2°F) lower than temperature at sea level for each increase of 300 m (1000 feet) in elevation. Temperature in brackets refers to adjustment, if necessary.

Availability of Canadian Fresh Fruits and Vegetables

Legend: ■ Peak | ▤ Good | * Low | ☐ Not Available

	J	F	M	A	M	J	J	A	S	O	N	D
Apples	▤	▤	▤	▤	▤	*	*	*	▤	▤	▤	▤
Apricots							■	■				
Asparagus					■	■	*					
Beans							▤	■	▤	*		
Beets	▤	▤	▤	*	*	*	■	■	■	▤	▤	▤
Blueberries								■	▤			
Broccoli							▤	■	■	■	*	
Brussels Sprouts							*	▤	■	■	■	
Cabbage	▤	▤	▤	*	*	▤	▤	■	■	▤	▤	▤
Cantaloupes								■	▤			
Carrots	▤	▤	▤	*			*	■	▤	▤	▤	▤
Cauliflower						*	▤	■	■	■	*	
Celery								▤	■	■	*	
Cherries						*	■	*				
Corn (sweet)							▤	■	▤	*		
Cranberries									■	*	▤	
Cucumbers			*	▤	▤	▤	▤	■	▤	*	*	
Eggplant							*	▤	■	▤	*	
Endive	*	*	*	*		*	■	■	▤	▤		*
Fiddleheads					■	▤						
Garlic							*	▤	■	*		
Grapes (table)								*	■	▤		
Leeks	▤	*	*	*	*	*	*	▤	■	■	▤	▤
Lettuce				*	▤	■	■	■	*	*		
Mixed Melons								■	*			
Mushrooms	▤	▤	▤	▤	▤	▤	▤	▤	▤	▤	▤	▤
Onions	▤	▤	▤	*	*	*	*	▤	■	■	▤	▤
Parsley	*	*	*	*	*	*	▤	■	▤	▤	*	*
Parsnips	▤	▤	▤	*	*		*		▤	▤	▤	▤
Peaches							*	▤	■			
Pears	▤	▤	*	*				▤	■	▤	▤	▤
Peas							▤	■				
Peppers							*	▤	■	▤		
Plums & Prunes							*	■	▤	*		
Potatoes	▤	▤	▤	▤	▤	*	*	▤	■	▤	▤	▤
Pumpkins									■	■	*	
Radishes				*	*	■	■	▤	*	*		
Raspberries							▤	■	*	*		
Rhubarb	*	▤	▤	*	▤	■	*	*				
Rutabagas	▤	▤	▤	▤	▤	*	*		▤	▤	▤	▤
Spinach					*	▤	■	■	▤	▤	*	*
Squash	*	*					*	▤	■	■	▤	*
Strawberries						■	■					
Tomatoes					*	▤	▤	■	▤	▤	*	

N Glossary of Food and Cooking Terms

À La Mode: In style. Desserts à la mode are served with ice cream; meats cooked à la mode are braised with vegetables and served with gravy.

Age:
1. To tenderize meat by allowing it to hang for a specified length of time in carefully controlled conditions.
2. To store cheese until it is mature and the flavour has developed.
3. To store wine to improve the flavour.

Al Dente: Italian term used to describe pasta that is briefly cooked until it offers a slight resistance to the bite.

Amandine: Dishes containing or garnished with almonds.

Aspic: Jelly made from beef, veal, chicken or fish stock that gels naturally because of dissolved gelatine; a cold dish coated or moulded with flavoured stock; a firm gel made with vegetable juices (e.g. tomato), seasonings and gelatine.

Bake: To cook food items by dry heat (uncovered) in an oven including breads, cakes, fruits, vegetable casseroles, pâtés, ham and fish. When applied to most meats and poultry, it is called roasting.

Barbecue: To roast or broil food on a rack or spit over coals, or under a heat unit. The food is often brushed with a seasoned sauce during cooking.

Baste: To moisten food with melted butter, fat or liquid while it cooks. Basting helps prevent the surface from drying out while also adding flavour.

Batter: A mixture of relatively thin consistency, made of flour, liquid and other ingredients.

Bavarian: A moulded cold dessert made with gelatine, eggs, (whipping) cream and flavourings.

Beat: To make a mixture smooth by incorporating air with rapid, regular motion, using a fork, wire whisk, spoon, hand beater or mixer.

Bisque: A thick, rich cream soup usually made with shellfish or puréed vegetables.

Blanch: To immerse foods briefly in boiling water, followed by a quick cooling in cold water, used to loosen or remove skins of fruit and vegetables and as a technique prior to preservation to delay spoilage.

Blend: To stir two or more unlike ingredients together to form a mixture in which separate ingredients are indistinguishable (homogeneous); to prepare food in a blender.

Boil: To cook food in liquid at or above the boiling point.

Bombe: A dessert of frozen mixtures arranged and frozen in a conical shaped mould. The mould is usually lined with ice cream, then filled with a bombe mixture of a different flavour to which diced fruit or other ingredients may be added.

Bone: To remove bones from meat, fish or poultry.

Bouillabaisse: A hearty stew made with several kinds of fish and shellfish.

Braise: To cook food by low heat in a small amount of liquid in a covered pan or to brown foods in fat, then cook (often in a covered casserole) with a small amount of liquid.

Bread: To coat with bread crumbs, cracker crumbs or cornmeal. Food may first be floured, then dipped in beaten egg or other liquid to help crumbs adhere.

Brochette: A skewer. Food cooked "en brochette" is cooked on a skewer.

Broil: To cook food under direct heat on a rack or spit.

Broth (Bouillon): A thin, clear savory essence drawn from a combination of meats, vegetables and herbs that are simmered in water and then strained.

Brown: To cook food usually in a small amount of fat, over moderate heat, until it darkens in colour.

Brush: To coat very lightly with liquid (e.g. melted butter) using a pastry brush.

Candy: To cook fruits or vegetables in syrup, or fat and sugar. Candied refers to fruits or vegetables cooked this way.

Caramelize: To stir sugar or foods containing sugar in a skillet over low heat until it melts and develops characteristic flavour and golden-brown colour.

Carve: To cut meat or poultry in slices or pieces for serving.

Charlotte: An elegant dessert made with a mould or spring-form pan lined with ladyfingers or strips of sponge cake, then filled with Bavarian, chiffon, mousse or other cream, jelly or ice mixture.

Chiffon: Custard gel to which beaten egg whites are added. Egg yolks are cooked with gelatine as it dissolves, to make a custard gel. The gel is chilled until thickened, then egg whites folded in.

Chill: To refrigerate food or let it stand in ice or ice water until cold.

Chop: To cut food into small pieces with a knife, blender or food processor.

Coat: To sprinkle food with, or dip it into, flour, sauce etc., until covered.

Coddle: To simmer gently in water just below the boiling point, four to six minutes (e.g. egg).

Combine: To stir two or more like ingredients together to form a mixture of uniform consistency in which separate ingredients are distinguishable.

Consistency of mixture: Refers to the appearance and texture of a mixture to describe whether it should be soft, stiff, etc.

Consommé: A very clear, richly flavoured broth, usually beef, that has been clarified of all fat.

Cool: To allow mixture to come to room temperature.

Cream: To make soft, smooth and creamy by beating with a spoon or mixer, usually applied to blending sugar and a fat, or when cooking food in or serving it with a white or "cream" sauce. Consumer and Corporate Affairs Canada states "...care should be exercised in the use of the word "butter", "cream" or "creamy" in the name of a food or in descriptions relating to that food. They should not be used to describe a food that is or has been made in part of cream or butter unless the food contains a significant amount of cream or butter. However, when it is clear that these terms refer to texture, form and the like and not to the butter or cream content then their use may be acceptable". (e.g. peanut butter.)

Crêpe: A thin, delicate pancake.

Croquette: A mixture of chopped or minced food, usually shaped as a cone or ball, coated with egg and crumbs, then deep-fried.

Crush: To extract juice with press, mallet or side of knife.

Cube: To cut food into small cubes (e.g. about 1 cm / ½ in. square); to cut surface of meat in checkered pattern to increase tenderness e.g. cubing steak.

Cut in: To distribute solid fat in flour or flour mixture by using pastry blender or two knives scissor fashion until flour-coated fat particles are of desired size.

Deep-fry: To cook food in hot fat deep enough for food to float in (see Fats, Oils and Shortenings).

Dice: To cut food into very small uniform pieces.

Dilute: To make less strong, e.g. fresh lemon juice is diluted with water for lemonade.

Dissolve: To make a solution; to melt or liquefy.

Divan: A type of casserole layered with broccoli or asparagus on the bottom, a protein food such as chicken or egg, covered with cheese sauce.

Dough: A mixture of liquid and flour that is stiff enough to be handled or kneaded.

Dot: To scatter bits of fat (e.g. butter or margarine) over surface of food, similar to basting.

Draw: To remove entrails from and clean, poultry or game. Drawn fish are whole fish that have been cleaned (eviscerated) but not boned.

Dredge: To cover or coat food with flour, cornmeal or other fine substances.

Drippings: Fat and juice given off by meat or poultry as it cooks.

Dust: To sprinkle lightly with flour or sugar.

Eviscerate: To remove internal organs of fish or poultry.

Flake: To break into small pieces, usually with a fork.

Flame: To ignite warmed alcoholic beverages over food, also known as flambé.

Flesh: The inside or edible portion of whole fruits and vegetables.

Flute: To make decorative indentations (e.g. on edge of piecrust).

Fold: To combine one ingredient with another very gently to avoid loss of air. The motion consists of cutting vertically through mixture with spoon or spatula and sliding across bottom of bowl and up the side, turning over. Proper folding may be a key to recipe success.

Fry: To cook food over high heat in a small amount of fat.

Gazpacho: A cold Spanish soup made with tomatoes and other fresh vegetables.

Glaze: To coat with a glossy mixture.

Goulash: A type of beef stew with onion and paprika.

Grate: To rub food on a grater (or chop in blender or food processor) to produce fine, medium or coarse particles.

Gratin: A French term defining brown crust formed by baking or broiling bread crumbs, cheese, butter on top of a casserole or other dish.

Grease: To rub surface of pan or dish with fat to keep food from sticking.

Grill: To cook food on a rack by direct heat; SI term for barbecue.

Grind: To reduce to particles in food grinder, blender or food processor.

Jardinière: French term meaning garnished with vegetables.

Julienne: French term used to describe vegetables cut in long, thin strips.

Kabob: Food, usually meat, poultry or vegetable, threaded on a skewer.

Knead: To work dough with hands by folding it over on itself, pushing down and away with heels of hands, turning dough one-quarter turn after each folding and pushing motion.

Kosher: Food ritually fit for eating in accordance with Jewish law.

Lard: To insert match-like strips of fat called lardoons, into gashes in the side of uncooked lean meat by means of a larding needle or skewer; to place fat on top of meat.

Lukewarm: A temperature of about 35°C (95°F). Lukewarm water feels neither hot nor cold when in contact with inside of wrist.

Lyonnaise: French term used for vegetables prepared with onion.

Marinate: To let stand in a marinade (usually a mixture of oil, lemon juice or vinegar and seasonings).

Mash: To beat food (e.g. potatoes) into a smooth purée. The process is usually done with a fork or potato masher.

Meringue: A mixture of stiffly beaten egg whites and sugar; the baked soft mixture on desserts or the baked "hard" mixture as a dessert shell.

Meunière: French term used to describe foods prepared with a sauce of butter, lemon juice and parsley.

Mince: To chop food into very fine pieces.

Mix: To stir two or more like ingredients together to form a mixture which has either distinguishable or indistinguishable ingredients.

Mocha: A flavouring of coffee; or made by combining coffee and chocolate.

Mousse: A cold dessert of clear gel to which whipped cream or beaten egg whites are added after the mixture has partially set.

Pan-broil: To cook food uncovered, over high heat on ungreased or lightly greased hot surface, pouring off accumulating fat.

Pan-fry: To cook food over high heat in a small amount of fat.

Parboil: To boil until partially cooked, usually before completing cooking by another method.

Parch: To brown grains by dry heat.

Pare: To remove skin or rind.

Parfait: A layered dessert made of fruit, syrup, ice cream, whipped cream, beaten egg whites, etc., served in a tall, slender glass.

Partially-set: Used to describe gelatine mixtures at the point in setting when the consistency resembles raw egg whites.

Pâté: A spread or loaf of ground seasoned meat, poultry, fish or vegetables.

Peel: To remove outer covering of foods by trimming with knife or vegetable peeler or by pulling off.

Pilaf: A seasoned rice, often with meat or poultry added.

Pipe: To press a mixture – generally some form of icing, whipping cream, creamed potatoes, etc., – through a pastry bag or tube.

Pit: To remove seed from whole fruit.

Poach: To cook food over low heat in simmering liquid.

Pour: The method used to transfer batter when it flows easily into the contours of a pan.

Preheat: To heat oven to desired temperature before cooking food.

Pressure-cook: To cook less tender cuts of meat, vegetables and canning low acid foods in steam under high pressure, using a special saucepan.

Pulp: The inside flesh or edible portion of fruits and vegetables when the natural state of the food is changed (e.g. cut, peeled, heated, cooked).

Punch down: To deflate a risen yeast dough by pushing it down with the fist.

Purée: To press food through a fine sieve or food mill; to blend in blender or food processor to a smooth, thick mixture; also, a thick mixture made from a puréed vegetable base.

Ragoût: A well-seasoned stew of meat and vegetables.

Reconstitute: To restore concentrated foods (non-fat dry milk, frozen fruit juices) to their normal state, usually by adding water.

Reduce: To decrease volume of liquid by rapid boiling in an uncovered pan.

Render: To remove fat from connective tissue over low heat.

Roast: To cook uncovered meat or poultry by dry heat, in an oven; not used for cooking ham, minced meat preparations or single serving portions of meat, poultry.

Roll-out: To lightly roll dough for pastry, pie etc., with a rolling pin to the required shape and thickness.

Rub-in: To mix fat with flour using fingers until the mixture is like bread crumbs.

Sauté: To cook in a skillet in a small amount of fat.

Scald: To heat liquid to just below the boiling point; to pour boiling water over food or dip food briefly in boiling water.

Scallopine: Small, thin pieces of meat sautéed or broiled until browned and tender.

Score: To cut shallow slits in surface of food to increase tenderness or to prevent fat covering from curling.

Scrape: To remove peel by a scraping movement with a sharp knife; used for new potatoes, new carrots, when it would be wasteful to peel.

Seal: To cover completely; or in pastry cooking to press cut ends together firmly, by various techniques.

Sear: To brown the surface of foods quickly.

Season: To add salt and pepper; the term used for preparing cooking equipment or bakeware.

Shred: To cut food into slivers or slender pieces using a knife or shredder.

Sieve: To push food (e.g. spinach, fruit) through a sieve to obtain a purée or to lighten flour and ensure it is free of lumps.

Simmer: To cook food over low heat in a liquid just below the boiling point in which bubbles form slowly and collapse just below the surface. This point may vary according to pot's size, depth, width, material, condition, cleanliness, water volume, the altitude, water hardness and personal interpretation of the individual. The normal simmer at sea level at normal atmospheric pressure is about 90°C (195°F); a high simmer, about 100°C (210°F); medium simmer, about 80°C (180°F).

Skim: To remove fat or film from surface of food.

Sliver: To cut food into long, thin pieces.

Snip: To cut with scissors into very fine pieces.

Snows: Clear gels to which unbeaten egg whites are added after the mixture has partially set. The mixture is then beaten stiff and chilled until completely set (sometimes called "sponge").

Spread: The method used to work a heavy, thick mixture into an even layer in a pan.

Steam: To cook food on a rack or in a colander over steaming hot water in a covered pan.

Steep: To allow a substance to stand in a liquid below the boiling point for the purpose of extracting flavour, colour or other qualities.

Stew: To cook food over low heat in a simmering liquid.

Stir: To mix ingredients with a circular motion.

Stir-fry: To cook sliced food quickly, Chinese-style in a wok or skillet.

Stock: Made the same as broth; it is meant to serve as a basis for soup, as a braising medium or as a sauce base.

Strain:
1. To remove food from liquid, e.g. vegetables when cooked.

2. To remove bones from stock, etc.

Stroganoff: A type of casserole with noodles, onions, mushrooms and meat (often beef strips) in a sauce with a sour cream base.

Toast: To brown by direct heat or in a hot oven.

Torte: A cake or meringue-type dessert, usually rich in eggs and nuts.

Toss: To mix foods lightly with a lifting motion.

Truss: To secure poultry with string or skewers, to hold its shape while cooking.

Turn: The method used to gently "pour" a mixture, which easily loses volume, into a pan.

Turnovers: Large or small unbaked flaky pastry folded over filling and baked. Fillings may be fruits or various forms of meats, poultry or fish.

Whip: To beat rapidly with mixer, wire whisks or hand beater, to incorporate air and increase volume.

Whips: Clear gels chilled until partially set, then beaten fluffy.

O Potential Computer Usage For Recipe Development

Many food professionals are discovering computer recipe assessment and storage of recipe data is the future direction of recipe research. The development and acceptance of sophisticated computer technology is having an impact on our society similar to that of the industrial revolution. Computers are saving time, one of our most limiting commodities, as well as releasing time for creative and innovative accomplishments. Home economists welcome the response and innovation that this new tool provides.

Software is available in a wide variety of home economics areas, including diet analysis. The Canadian Nutrient File, Health and Welfare Canada, is a data base which lists nutrients and nutrient related information (such as calories included in most common foods). Use of this program enables the home economist to promote wise choices of foods to include regularly in meal plans. Foods or ingredients listed could suggest wider or alternate choices for food professionals who are developing recipes to highlight a featured product.

Nutrition software programmes are also available, designed to compliment the Canadian Nutrient File, its American counterpart or professional nutrition education programs. The Organization for Nutrition Education provides current Canadian information.

Nutritional assessment, writing or editing recipes with a computer or word processor can produce greater accuracy and time efficiency. A company or institution can program its particular guidelines for recipe format into the computer; the machine prints out a specific format or self-corrects a recipe input. For example, standard abbreviations or imperial/metric replacement values would be readily accessible.

The Food Advisory Division, Agriculture Canada, has models of computer files for all its consumer and quantity recipes developed since 1978. (See Part III – Recipe Copy Presentation, ii. Quantity Food Service.) Both are standard recipe formats with metric measures only; they vary slightly but are cross-referenced. The six digit numbering system defines the yield and allows computer nutrient analysis of the recipe using the Agriculture Nutrient Analysis Program (AGNAP).

Coding differentiates recipes developed in metric measures and those adapted from imperial measures. Alternate recipe names are also coded. For the computer file, method steps are listed parallel to ingredients and measures. Two-part recipes have similar alignments. Quantity recipes have four columns – the ingredient, its weight, volume and corresponding method. Method is written in a single following paragraph for consumer recipes. Recipe yields are always included, usually four servings for consumer recipes and 50 for quantity recipes. If total volume is difficult to determine (e.g. soups, squares or casseroles), serving size is given. Cookies, squares, cakes and breads have yields in number. Pickles, relishes, jams, jellies, sauces and beverages have yields in volume. Recipes in which the amount of meat is expressed in weight, have serving sizes in weight. Recipe variations are coded as new recipes and filed under the appropriate category. Recipes are dated by latest accepted recipe test. Note is made of recipes used in promotional publications. Translated recipes are filed by number on card files.

Computers will soon be indispensable for storage of recipes or recipe data in homes as well as offices. Computer files are now commercially available for this purpose. Recipes stored in this way are more readily accessible than when located in card files, folders or books. By cross-referencing recipes in the computer, a single command can be given to call up recipes with one dominant ingredient (e.g. eggs, beef or cheese). Possible cooking methods (fondue, no-bake or barbecue), substitutions or equivalents programmed in are also more easily accessible.

Whatever the specific application, the computer in recipe development is potentially an invaluable tool.

part VI

Substitutions and Equivalents

Metric data is presented as reasonable replacement values for the food professional who develops metric recipes or adapts recipes to the metric system.

Ingredient measure, when offered to the client or consumer should give metric equivalents in hard conversion (rounded equivalents), as recommended by the Metric Committee of the Canadian Home Economics Association. During certain intermediate phases of recipe testing, soft metric conversion (exact equivalents) may be necessary.

A Standard Abbreviations/Symbols

Metric*

litre	L
millilitre	mL
kilogram	kg
gram	g
degree Celsius	°C
centimetre	cm
hour	h
minute	min
second	s

Note: No periods.

Imperial**

cup	*not abbreviated*
tablespoon	*tbsp.*
teaspoon	*tsp.*
pound	*lb.*
ounce	*oz.*
fluid ounce	*fl. oz.*
pint	*pt.*
quart	*qt.*
gallon	*gal.*
degree Fahrenheit	*°F*
peck	*pk.*
bushel	*bu.*
inch	*in. or "*
hour	*hr.*
minute	*min.*
second	*sec.*

**Note: Do not omit periods.*
Plural form of abbreviations/symbols is same.

General

f.d.	*few drops*
f.g.	*few grains*
A.P.	*as purchased*
E.P.	*edible portion*

3 Kitchen Measure Equivalents

1. Volume (Capacity) Equivalents

a few grains, dash	=	*less than ⅛ teaspoon*	4 tablespoons	=	*¼ cup*
60 drops	=	*1 teaspoon*	5⅓ tablespoons	=	*⅓ cup*
1 teaspoon	=	*⅓ tablespoon*	8 tablespoons	=	*½ cup*
1 tablespoon	=	*3 teaspoons*	16 tablespoons	=	*1 cup*
2 tablespoons	=	*1 fluid ounce*	1 cup	=	*8 fluid ounces*

	Units	Imperial*/U.S. Volume	Metric Volume
1 mL		.035 (Cdn.) fl. oz.	.001 L
		.034 (U.S.) fl. oz.	.001 L
1 L		35.2 (Cdn.) fl. oz.	1 000 mL
		33.8 (U.S.) fl. oz.	1 000 mL
1 (Cdn.) fluid oz.			28.4 mL
1 (U.S.) fluid oz.			29.57 mL
1 teaspoon			5 mL
3 teaspoons	1 tablespoon		15 mL
1 (Cdn.) cup		8 (Cdn.) fl. oz.	227 mL
1 (U.S.) cup**		8 (U.S.) fl. oz.	237 mL
1 (Cdn.) pint	2½ (Cdn.) cups	20 (Cdn.) fl. oz.	.568 L
1 (U.S.) pint	2 (U.S.) cups	16 (U.S.) fl. oz.	.473 L
1 (Cdn.) quart	5 (Cdn.) cups	40 (Cdn.) fl. oz.	1.136 L
1 (U.S.) quart	4 (U.S.) cups	32 (U.S.) fl. oz.	.946 L
1 (Cdn.) gallon	20 (Cdn.) cups	160 (Cdn.) fl. oz.	4.546 L
1 (U.S.) gallon	16 (U.S.) cups	128 (U.S.) fl. oz.	3.785 L

Common usage of term = Canadian measures. However, 1 British Imperial cup = 10 fl. oz.
**Used for Canadian and U.S. recipes.*

Dry Measure – Large Quantity Fruits and Vegetables
Be careful not to confuse dry measure pints and quarts with liquid measure pints and quarts.
The former are about one-sixth larger than the latter. Dry measure is used for raw fruit and vegetables,
when dealing with fairly large quantities.

1 quart	=	2 pints	=	1.136 L
8 quarts	=	1 (Cdn.) peck	=	9.092 L
4 pecks	=	1 (Cdn.) bushel	=	36.369 L

2. Weight Equivalents

1 oz.	=	28.4 g		
1 lb.	=	16 oz.	=	454 g
1 kg	=	1 000 g	=	2.2 lb.

Note: For reasonable metric replacement values (rounded kitchen measures), see Part IV – Metric Recipe Development and Style Guide.

Note: Equivalents (or reasonable replacement values) are approximate and serve only as a guide. Calculations are based on hard metric conversion.

Food	Amount Before Preparation	Approximate Measure After Preparation
Almonds	500 g (1 lb.) in shell	*300 mL (1¼ cups) shelled*
	500 g (1 lb.)	*650 mL (2⅔ cups) ground*
Apples	1 medium	*250 mL (1 cup) sliced or diced* *4 or 5 apple rings*
	3 to 4 medium	*375 mL (1½ cups) apple sauce*
Apricots	1 medium	*50 mL (¼ cup) sliced*
Avocados	1 medium	*300 mL (1¼ cup) chopped*
	1 medium	*125-175 mL (½-¾ cup) mashed*
Bananas	3 medium	*500 mL (2 cups) sliced* *250 mL (1 cup) purée*
Beans,		
kidney	500 g (1 lb.) or 375 mL (1½ cups)	*2.3 L (9 cups) cooked*
lima	500 g (1 lb.) or 625 mL (2½ cups)	*1.5 L (6 cups) cooked*
navy	500 g (1 lb.) or 625 mL (2½ cups)	*1.5 L (6 cups) cooked*
green	500 g (1 lb.) or 750 mL (3 cups)	*625 mL (2½ cups) cooked*
Bread, for crumbs	1 slice	*175 mL (¾ cup) soft or 50 mL (¼ cup) fine dry*
Cabbage	500 g (1 lb.) or 1 small	*1.3 L (5 cups) shredded*
Carrots	6 medium or 500 g (1 lb.)	*750 mL (3 cups) shredded or* *625 mL (2½ cups) diced*
Celery	1 medium bunch	*1.1 L (4½ cups) chopped*
Cheese,		
blue	113 g (4 oz.)	*250 mL (1 cup) crumbled*
hard	113 g (4 oz.)	*250 mL (1 cup) shredded or cubed*
Chicken	1.5 kg (3½ lb.) drawn chicken	*650 mL (2 cups) cooked, diced*
Chocolate	1 square	*60 mL (4 tbsp.) grated*
Coffee	500 g (1 lb.)	*10 L (40 cups) brewed*
Corn	1 medium ear	*125 mL (½ cup) kernels cut from cob*
Cornmeal	250 mL (1 cup)	*1 L (4 cups) cooked*

Food	Amount Before Preparation	Approximate Measure After Preparation
Crackers,		
Graham	14 squares	*250 mL (1 cup) finely crushed*
Saltine	28 squares	*250 mL (1 cup) crushed*
Figs	500 g (1 lb.)	*650 mL (2⅔ cups) chopped*
Gingersnaps	15 cookies	*250 mL (1 cup) finely crushed*
Green peppers	1 large	*250 mL (1 cup) diced*
Lemons	1 medium	*50 mL (3 tbsp.) juice* *10 mL (2 tsp.) peel*
Limes	1 medium	*25 mL (2 tbsp.) juice* *7 mL (1½ tsp.) peel*
Macaroni	250 mL (1 cup)	*625 mL (2½ cups) cooked*
Mushrooms	500 g (1 lb.) or 1.5 L (6 cups)	*1.5 L (6 cups) sliced raw or* *500 mL (2 cups) cooked*
Noodles	250 mL (1 cup)	*425 mL (1¾ cups) cooked*
Orange	1 medium	*50-75 mL (¼-⅓ cup) juice* *25-30 mL (2-2½ tbsp.) peel*
Onions,		
cooking	1 medium	*125 mL (½ cup) chopped uncooked*
green	1 bunch	*125 mL (½ cup) sliced*
Peaches	1 medium	*125 mL (½ cup) sliced*
Pears	1 medium	*125 mL (½ cup) sliced*
Peas,		
dried	500 g (1 lb.) or 625 mL (2½ cups)	*1.5 L (6 cups) cooked*
split	500 mL (2 cups) or 500 g (1 lb.)	*1.3 L (5 cups) cooked*
Pecans, shell	500 g (1 lb.)	*500 mL (2 cups) shelled*
Prunes	500 g (1 lb.)	*500 mL (2 cups) cooked and drained*
Potatoes	500 g (1 lb.)	*500 mL (2 cups) cooked and mashed* *650 mL (2⅔ cups) cubed uncooked*
Pomegranate	1 medium	*125 mL (½ cup) pulpy seeds*
Popcorn	50 mL (¼ cup)	*1.3 L (5 cups) popped*
Radishes	1 large bunch	*250 mL (1 cup) sliced*
Rice,		
long grain	250 mL (1 cup)	*750 mL (3 cups) cooked*
quick cooking	250 mL (1 cup)	*500 mL (2 cups) cooked*

Food	Amount Before Preparation	Approximate Measure After Preparation
Rhubarb	500 g (1 lb.)	*500 mL (2 cups) chopped uncooked*
Spinach	500 g (1 lb.)	*3 L (12 cups) uncooked* *375 mL (1½ cups) cooked*
Spaghetti	226 g (8 oz.)	*1 L (4 cups) cooked*
Strawberries	1 L (4 cups) whole	*750 mL (3 cups sliced)*
Tea	500 g (1 lb.)	*31 L (125 cups) brewed*
Tomatoes	1 medium	*125 mL (½ cup) cooked*
Vanilla wafers	22 cookies	*250 mL (1 cup) finely crushed*
Walnuts	500 g (1 lb.) in shell	*375 mL (1½ cups) shelled*
Whipping cream	250 mL (1 cup)	*500 mL (2 cups) whipped*
Zucchini	1 medium	*250 mL (1 cup) sliced uncooked*

D Substitutions For Common Foods

Readily available, popular or less common ingredients may be exchanged or substituted during recipe development. Occasionally, suggestions for ingredient substitutions are suggested in recipe copy. In all cases, the recipe with the substitution requires thorough testing.
Note: Calculations are based on hard metric conversion.

Ingredients	Amount	Substitutions
Baking Powder (Rising Equivalent)	5 mL (1 tsp.)	*2 mL (⅓ tsp.) baking soda plus 2 mL (½ tsp.) cream of tartar* OR *1 mL (¼ tsp.) baking soda plus 125 mL (½ cup) buttermilk or yoghurt*
Double Acting, SAS	5 mL (1 tsp.)	*7 mL (1½ tsp.) phosphate or tartrate*
Butter	250 mL (1 cup)	*200 mL (⅘ cup) fat, clarified* OR *175 mL (¾ cup) chicken fat, clarified* OR *225 mL (⅞ cup) cottonseed, nut, corn oil, solid or liquid* OR *225 mL (⅞ cup) lard plus 2 mL (½ tsp.) salt* OR *200-225 mL (⅘-⅞ cup) drippings*
	226 g (8 oz.)	*210 g (7.4 oz.) hydrogenated fats*
Buttermilk	250 mL (1 cup)	*250 mL (1 cup) plain yoghurt*
Chocolate, unsweetened	28 g (1 oz.)	*50 mL (3 tbsp.) cocoa, plus 15 mL (1 tbsp.) butter or margarine*
Cornstarch	15 mL (1 tbsp.) for thickening	*25 mL (2 tbsp.) all-purpose flour*
Corn syrup	250 mL (1 cup)	*250 mL (1 cup) granulated sugar plus 50 mL (¼ cup) liquid*
Cracker crumbs	175 mL (¾ cup)	*250 mL (1 cup) bread crumbs*
Cream, sour	250 mL (1 cup)	*50 mL (3 tbsp.) butter plus 225 mL (⅞ cup) sour milk or 250 mL (1 cup) plain yoghurt*
whipping (heavy) (to be whipped)	250 mL (1 cup)	*500 mL (2 cups) whipped dessert topping*
	250 mL (1 cup)	*175 mL (¾ cup) milk plus 75 mL (⅓ cup) butter*

Ingredients	Amount	Substitutions
Eggs, whole	1 large	*2 egg yolks* *OR* *40 mL (2½ tbsp.) dried plus 40 mL (2½ tbsp.) water* *OR* *1 extra large, 1 medium or 2 small*
	2 large	*2 extra large, 2 medium or 3 small*
	3 large	*3 extra large, 4 medium or 4 small*
	4 large	*3 extra large, 5 medium or 6 small*
	5 large	*4 extra large, 6 medium or 7 small*
	6 large	*5 extra large, 7 medium or 8 small*
Egg white	white of 1 large	*25 mL (2 tbsp.) thawed frozen egg white*
Egg yolk	yolk of 1 large	*20 mL (4 tsp.) thawed frozen egg yolk* *OR* *25 mL (2 tbsp.) dry plus 10 mL (2 tsp.) water*
Flour, sifted **all-purpose**	250 mL (1 cup)	*250 mL (1 cup), plus 25 mL (2 tbsp.) cake flour*
cake	250 mL (1 cup)	*225 mL (⅞ cup) all-purpose flour*
Garlic	1 small clove	*0.5 mL (⅛ tsp.) powder*
Honey	250 mL (1 cup)	*300 mL (1¼ cups) granulated sugar plus 50 mL (¼ cup) liquid*
Lemon, **juice**	5 mL (1 tsp.)	*2 mL (½ tsp.) vinegar*
peel	5 mL (1 tsp.)	*2 mL (½ tsp.) lemon extract*
Milk, **whole**	250 mL (1 cup)	*125 mL (½ cup) evaporated milk plus 125 mL (½ cup) water* *OR* *50 mL (¼ cup) powdered milk plus 250 mL (1 cup) water plus 7 mL (1½ tsp.) butter*
sour	250 mL (1 cup)	*15 mL (1 tbsp.) vinegar or lemon juice plus milk to make 250 mL (1 cup); let stand 5-10 min.*
Onion	1 small	*5 mL (1 tsp.) onion powder* *OR* *5 mL (1 tsp.) minced dried onion*
Sugar, granulated	250 mL (1 cup)	*250 mL (1 cup) packed brown sugar* *OR* *500 mL (2 cups) sifted powdered sugar* *OR* *60 mL (4 tbsp.) sugar substitute*

Ingredient	Amount	Substitutions
Tapioca	10 mL (2 tsp.)	*15 mL (1 tbsp.) flour*
Tomato sauce	250 mL (1 cup)	*175 mL (¾ cup) tomato paste plus 250 mL (1 cup) water*
Yeast	1 package active dry yeast	*1 cake compressed yeast*
Yoghurt	250 mL (1 cup)	*250 mL (1 cup) buttermilk*

E Volume and Weight Equivalents for Common Foods

Note: Equivalents (or reasonable replacement values) are approximate and serve only as a guide. Calculations are based on hard metric conversion.

	Measure Equivalents	
Ingredients	Volume	Weight
Almonds,		
unblanched, whole	250 mL (1 cup)	*170 g (6 oz.)*
ground	650 mL (2⅔ cups)	*500 g (1 lb.)*
slivered	1.4 L (5⅔ cups)	*500 g (1 lb.)*
blanched, whole	250 mL (1 cup)	*150 g (5⅓ oz.)*
Apples	3 medium	*500 g (1 lb.)*
Apricots	9-10 medium	*500 g (1 lb.)*
Bananas	3-4 medium	*500 g (1 lb.)*
Beans –		
dried kidney, lima, navy	650 mL (2⅔ cups)	*500 g (1 lb.)*
Butter	500 mL (2 cups)	*500 g (1 lb.)*
Cheese,		
cottage	250 mL (1 cup)	*250 g (½ lb.)*
cream	500 mL (2 cups)	*500 g (1 lb.)*
Cherries – candied	625 mL (2½ cups)	*500 g (1 lb.)*
Chocolate chips	1 square	*28 g (1 oz.)*
	250 mL (1 cup)	*170 g (6 oz.)*
Cocoa	1 L (4 cups)	*500 g (1 lb.)*
Coconut – shredded	325 mL (1⅓ cups)	*113 g (4 oz.)*
Cranberries	1.3 L (5 cups)	*500 g (1 lb.)*
Dates – pitted	625 mL (2½ cups)	*500 g (1 lb.)*
Eggs, whole,		
large	5	*250 mL (1 cup)*
medium	6	*250 mL (1 cup)*
small	7	*250 mL (1 cup)*
Egg whites,		
large	8	*250 mL (1 cup)*
medium	10-11	*250 mL (1 cup)*
small	11-12	*250 mL (1 cup)*
Egg yolks,		
large	12	*250 mL (1 cup)*
medium	13-14	*250 mL (1 cup)*
small	15-16	*250 mL (1 cup)*

	Measure Equivalents	
Ingredients	Volume	Weight
Flour,		
all-purpose	875 mL (3½ cups)	500 g (1 lb.)
cake and pastry	1.2 mL (4¾ cups)	500 g (1 lb.)
graham	1.1 L (4⅓ cups)	500 g (1 lb.)
rye	1 L (4¼ cups)	500 g (1 lb.)
whole wheat	1 L (4¼ cups)	500 g (1 lb.)
Lard	500 mL (2 cups)	500 g (1 lb.)
Macaroni	1.3 L (5 cups)	500 g (1 lb.)
Marshmallow – miniature	1.3 L (5 cups)	300 g (10.5 oz.)
Milk,		
whole dry solids	875 mL (3½ cups)	500 g (1 lb.)
dry nonfat solids	1 L (4 cups)	500 g (1 lb.)
Oatmeal	1.3 L (5 cups)	500 g (1 lb.)
Peanut Butter	425 mL (1¾ cups)	500 g (1 lb.)
Raisins – dry, loosely packed	750 mL (3 cups)	500 g (1 lb.)
Rice – raw	500 mL (2⅛ cups)	500 g (1 lb.)
Shortening – hydrogenated	325 mL (2⅓ cups)	500 g (1 lb.)
Sugar,		
brown, light pack	750 mL (3 cups)	500 g (1 lb.)
brown, firm pack	500 mL (2 cups)	500 g (1 lb.)
granulated	550 mL (2¼ cups)	500 g (1 lb.)
icing, sifted	1 L (4¼ cups)	500 g (1 lb.)
Walnuts,		
halves	1 L (4 cups)	500 g (1 lb.)
chopped	750 mL (3 cups)	500 g (1 lb.)

Bibliography

Of the many sources researched, the following proved especially useful:

Agriculture Canada, A Guide to Buying and Storage of Canadian Foods. 1977.

Agriculture Canada, Publication 1720E, Canada's Food Grades. 1982.

Agriculture Canada, Food Advisory Division, Guide for Converting Recipes to the Metric System. (Revised 1981).

Agriculture Canada, Food Advisory Division, Recipe Information Guide (Revised 1984).

American Home Economics Association, Handbook of Food Preparation (8th ed.). Washington 1980.

Amerine, Maynard A., Rose Marie Pangborn and **Edward B. Roessler,** Principles of Sensory Evaluation of Food. Academic Press, Inc. New York 1965.

Canadian Home Economics Association, A Metric Guide for Cookware and Bakeware. 1977.

Canadian Home Economics Association Metric Committee, Style Guide for Metric Recipes. Ottawa 1975 (Revised 1980).

Cardinal Kitchens, A Division of Cardinal Biologicals Ltd. Don Mills. In-house resource material.

Consumer and Corporate Affairs Canada, Guide for Food Manufacturers and Advertisers. Ottawa 1984.

Culinary Arts Institute, The Canadian Family Cookbook. Delair Publishing Co., Inc. New York 1981.

de Man, John M., Principles of Food Chemistry. The Avi Publishing Co., Inc. Connecticut 1976.

Gibson, L.D., "The Psychology of Food: why we eat what we eat when we eat it." Food Technology, vol. 35, February 1981.

Good Housekeeping Books, The Good Housekeeping Cookbook. New York 1973.

Health and Welfare Canada, Canada's Food Guide Handbook. Ottawa 1982 (Revised).

Health and Welfare Canada, Health Protection and Food Laws. 1981 (Revised).

Kieren, Dianne K., "Home Economics in the computer age, are we ready?" Canadian Home Economics Journal (32) 4, Fall 1982.

Kriz, Caroline, Convection Cookery. 101 Productions. United States 1980.

Lake of the Woods Mills Ltd., A Guide to Good Cooking (25th ed.). Montreal.

Litton, Variable Power Microwave Cooking. United States 1975.

McCarthy, E. Jerome and **Stanley J. Shapiro,** Basic Marketing (3rd Canadian ed.). Irwin – Dorsey of Canada, Illinois 1983.

Meredith Corporation, Better Homes and Gardens New Cook Book. United States 1976.

Meredith Corporation, Better Homes and Gardens Complete Step by Step Cook Book. Iowa 1978.

Methven, Barbara, Recipe Conversion for Microwave. Publication Arts, Inc. Minnesota 1979.

Ontario Ministry of Agriculture and Food Home Economics Branch, A New Wave of Cooking. 1981.

Organization for Nutrition Education, Newsletter, vol. 5, no. 2, Winter 1984.

Pattinson, Nellie Lyle, Canadian Cook Book. (Revised by Helen Wattie and Elinor Donaldson Whyte.) McGraw-Hill Ryerson Ltd., 1977.

Rombauer, Irma S. and **Marion Rombauer Becker,** Joy of Cooking. Thomas Allen and Sons Ltd. Toronto 1972.

Statistics Canada, Urban Family Food Expenditure. Ottawa 1976.

Sunset Books, Microwave Cook Book. Lane Publishing Co. California 1976.

The Benjamin Co., Inc., Multi-Power Microwave Miracles from Sanyo. New York 1979.

The Benjamin Co., Inc., "Cookbook and Recipe Preferences: The Consumer Says", Presented at the Home Economists in Business Convention. Dallas, June 1980.

Wenzel, George L., Wenzel's Menu Maker (2nd ed.). CBF Publishing Co., Inc. Boston 1979.

The staff home economists of Cardinal Kitchens would like to thank the food professionals who offered their valuable contributions and encouragement in writing this handbook.

Index

A

B

C

D